THE MICRODISTILLERS' HANDBOOK

Gavin D. Smith

First published in 2018 by
Paragraph Publishing, 6 Woolgate Court,
St Benedicts Street, Norwich, Norfolk, NR2 4AP

www.paragraph.co.uk

ISBN 978-0-9926399-9-0

Acknowledgements
The publishers would like to thank all those microdistilleries who provided information for their case studies and to thank Gavin D. Smith for bringing this book together. They would also like to thank Pickering's Gin for supplying the front cover image.

Publisher: Damian Riley-Smith
Design: Tim A'Court, Mandy Farnell & Paul Beevis
Publishing Consultant: Rupert Wheeler

Printed in Great Britain by TJ International Ltd.

THE
MICRODISTILLERS'
HANDBOOK

Contents

Foreword

I n the summer of 2012 I looked out of the window of my Cotswolds farmhouse, mesmerised by a neighbouring field of spring barley waving in the breeze, and thought to myself "There's a lot of barley growing around here and no one making any whisky!" That daydream was the start of a six year journey which last week, saw our Cotswolds single malt whisky launch in over 200 Waitrose stores across the UK. There have been numerous surprises along the way, not least of which has been our 'journey to gin' in which a product we saw as secondary in our original business plan took off and is now selling four times the volume as our recently-launched whisky.

There were many other surprises, mostly good but some which presented significant challenges given my inexperience and that of our small team. It is a testament to the extraordinary growth of microdistilling in the UK that we now have *The Microdistiller's Handbook*, which I would have found extremely useful as I tried to figure out the many unknowns of this activity for which I had no relevant prior experience.

Reading through the Handbook I was amazed at the breadth of useful information, much of which I had to source from disparate places when I started out – from HMRC to marketing and PR agencies, to process engineering firms. No such resource like this was available back in 2013, when I decided to take the plunge and move forward. My introduction into the world of distilling came from a number of the sources also listed in this handbook – I took a class at the Institute of Brewing and Distilling (IBD) and eventually hired a few graduates from the Msc course in brewing and distilling at Heriot Watt university. But the greatest help in learning about what it takes to design, build and operate a distillery came from two wonderful consultants, Harry Cockburn and the late Dr. Jim Swan. Harry helped me through the engineering, along with Richard Forsyth Jr. while Jim provided us with invaluable insight into flavour profile and wood characteristics, all of which saved us years in ramping up to where we could make a truly fine new make spirit. I would highly recommend finding an experienced consultant to help you through that difficult first year while you set up for production.

Thanks to the resources in this book you will be able to gain an understanding of the business along with a number of the key areas which are critical to your success. There remains a significant tailwind benefitting the microdistilling industry; many people are drinking less, but want to drink better. They are looking for locally-made products with authenticity and artisanal quality, made by real people with interesting backstories and values. These elements are extremely difficult for the 'big guys' to provide as they do not exist naturally in the DNA of large corporations, which are much better positioned to 'pile it high and sell it cheap' – thereby commoditising brands which should ideally retain a degree of romance.

On the other hand, the 'big guys' should not be ignored, but rather studied for what it is they do best – sales, marketing, promotion and distribution. This will be the hardest hurdle for those who want to make the jump from a small regional distillery to a brand driven national player, and a number of successful distillers have decided that the best way to take this step is through acquisition by a large player. It is still early days for us at the Cotswolds Distillery, but we recognise that over the years our challenge will be to reinvest as much of our revenue as possible into sales, marketing and distribution in order to build our brand and grow our distribution. At the end of the day, as we have discovered, this business is more about your brand than your products.

My final advice is to understand the importance of scale in this business and to source the biggest kit you can possibly afford (and even bigger, if possible). No successful distiller has ever said "I wish I had bought smaller kit", and far too often the opposite is true. The corollary to that is you need to be aware of just how capital-hungry a business this is, particularly if you are making an aged product. So think through your marketing and brand plan, your capital plan and prepare for success by buying big kit. It's a far more difficult business than I could have ever imagined looking out that window back in 2012, but I remain as passionate as ever and I don't for a minute regret my decision.

Daniel Szor, CEO, Cotswolds Distillery
October 2018

Introduction

Had you walked into even the most well-heeled of British bars a decade ago the range of spirits on offer would have been very different to those in the same bar today.

Certainly, there would have been a reasonable selection of single malt whiskies available, especially north of the border, as the malt revolution had been gathering pace for some time, but you would not have found any English whiskies on the bar shelves, and as for gin and vodka, a few well-known names would have dominated, including Gordon's, Beefeater, Smirnoff and Absolut.

During the last ten years, however, things have changed significantly, with a gin revolution fuelled by the apparently insatiable appetite among consumers for cocktails. This had led to the emergence of new large-scale brands, but also many more that have developed almost under the radar, and even now may have only a comparatively local following.

For this is the era of the microdistiller, and while gin may often be his or her principal spirit of choice, vodkas, whiskies, rums and even sambucas have also been making their appearance. At the heart of the microdistilling revolution is a passion for provenance, which began with food and went on to embrace beer and then spirits. Buying local has become the antidote to soulless supermarket shopping for brands that could have come from almost anywhere in the world.

As is so often the case, Britain followed the USA in a pursuit of products with a story behind them, products made by identifiable individuals, and if those individuals happened to be working in your neighbourhood or town then the sense of identification was so much more palpable.

The revival of local brewing enterprises on both sides of the Atlantic were in some ways a response to the monopolies of companies such as AB InBev, which accounts for almost 30 per cent of all beer volumes sold globally, and in the UK, such enterprises tapped into the desire for beers of character and accountability that had been nurtured by the Campaign for Real Ale (CAMRA) over more than four decades.

Not that some of the new wave of UK brewers were interested in complying with the criteria for 'real ale.' Rather, they were keen to innovate in any way they could discover, using many varieties of hops and creating entirely new beer styles as well as reviving old ones.

Setting up a microbrewery is not particularly expensive, and licensing relatively easy to achieve, whereas the idea of creating a distillery appeared to be altogether more financially unviable, and HM Customs & Excise – now HM Revenue & Customs – was not in the business of licensing what might be seen almost as 'hobby' stills.

Today, the legislative culture has changed, and though there may still be many hoops to jump through to obtain a distilling licence and adhere to HMRC protocols, there is an acceptance among legislators and their representatives that microdistilling is essentially a force for good.

Similarly, there has been a realisation that creating a small-scale gin distillery, using bought-in neutral spirit, may not actually break the bank. Much depends on the property in which you plan to house the operation, and this is where farmers and brewers bent on diversification tend to score highly, as they usually have space available within existing buildings.

Needless to say, starting from scratch can be an expensive undertaking, particularly if you decide to take on an aesthetically pleasing but potentially wallet-emptying old building and convert it for use as a distillery. An anonymous industrial estate unit will be much cheaper, but hardly conducive to conducting guided tours or hosting masterclasses.

If you plan to make whisky, then not only do you have to factor in the compulsory three years minimum maturation period before you can sell it as 'whisky,' but also the additional costs associated with kitting out a distillery with a mash tun and fermentation vessels, as well as stills. Buying decent casks in which to age your spirit is also a significant expense. A conservative estimate for setting up a small-scale whisky distillery would probably be in the region of £150,000, and many entrants to the business have spent well into seven figures. Investment in whisky stocks is likely to be ten times the cost of the distillery.

Despite financial implications, there is no sign that the recent growth in microdistilling start-up ventures in the UK is beginning to slow down. Optimism remains strong, and most encouraging of all, while many new breweries have opened up only to close soon after, to date the microdistilling sector has seen very few casualties.

No matter how much you intend to invest in your microdistilling venture, it is important to take good advice at every stage of your journey, and in the pages ahead we try to steer would-be distillers in the right direction in terms of rules, regulations, requirements, ingredients, business administration, selling and the myriad other aspects of running a successful microdistillery.

If you do decide to take the plunge, then enjoy yourselves, hope that hard work and wisdom pay off, and most importantly of all, create some wonderful, individualistic spirits along the way.

Gavin Smith
October 2018

Chapter One
What is distilling?

According to The Oxford English Dictionary, 'distillation' is "The action of converting any substance or constituent of a substance into vapour by means of heat and condensing this by cooling into the liquid form, by means of an alembic, retort and receiver, or a still and refrigeratory, the extraction of the spirit essence or essential oil of any substance by the evaporation and condensation of its liquid solution; and, in a more generalised sense, the operation of separating by means of fire, and in closed vessels, the volatile distillation parts of any substance from the fixed parts, in order to the collection of the products."

In the 4th century BC Aristotle wrote in his Meteorology that "Seawater can be made potable by distillation as well and wine and other liquids can be submitted to the same process," and that process may date back as far as 2,000 BC.

Early distillation – to create medicines and perfumes rather than alcohol for consumption – is credited to China, Mesopotamia and Egypt, though there is evidence that the Chinese were distilling a beverage from rice by 800 BC, and it is thought that the Egyptians understood distillation in the time of Diocletian (AD 284–305). Some sources consider that the alembic still was invented around that time by Maria the Jewess, or Zosimo of Panopolis, an Egyptian alchemist and his sister Theosebeia, who invented many stills and reflux condensers.

Another school of thought suggests that the Arabians devised the alembic during the eighth or ninth centuries. 'Alembic' is a European corruption of 'al ambic' the term used by the Arabians, and based on the Greek word 'ambix,' – a vase with a small opening in it. The Arabians were probably the first to cool the tube leading from the still-head with water, making distillation significantly more efficient and predictable, and a further advance came in the form of a coiled cooling pipe, devised in the 11th century, and responsible for very effective conversion of vapour back into liquid.

The art of distillation is thought to have been introduced into Europe around 1150 by the Moors of Spain, though so much of the early history of distillation remains essentially a matter of conjecture, and other historians prefer the theory that the Turks took distillation to Europe during invasions in the 14th and 15th centuries. The Oxford English Dictionary offers the first English attestation of the term 'distillation' in 1390.

From their medicinal origins, spirits came to be seen as a means of promoting relaxation and general well-being, and were used at social gatherings and festivals. The Latin term 'acqua vitae' – water of life – became 'eau de vie' in French and in Scots Gaelic 'uisge beatha' – ultimately anglicised to 'whisky.'

Unsurprisingly, distillers worked with whatever fermentable substances were most readily available to them, and so the French developed cognac from grapes, the inhabitants of the Caribbean used sugar cane to make rum, and in Scotland and Ireland grain was turned into whisky, or whiskey. The first reference to Scotch whisky occurs in the Exchequer Rolls for 1494/95, where it is stated: "Eight bolls of malt to Friar John Cor wherewith to make aqua vitae."

Scotch and Irish

The debate about whether Scotch came before Irish whisk(e)y or vice versa remains hotly debated. It is recorded that in 1276 Sir Robert Savage of Bushmills fortified his troops prior to battle with "a mighty draught of uisce beathe," but on closer examination it becomes clear that the fortification came in the form of wine or beer. However, Queen Elizabeth I was thought to have had a taste for Irish whiskey, probably being introduced to the spirit by Sir Walter Raleigh, who recorded in 1617 receiving in County Cork "a supreme present of a 32-gallon cask of the Earl of Cork's home-distilled uisce beatha."

Back in Scotland, there was a clear split between Lowland and Highland whisky making, with many pieces of excise legislation intended to curb illicit distillation in the Highlands, where distilling operations tended to be smaller than those in the Lowlands, and the remote nature of much of the countryside made concealment of whisky-making without a licence relatively easy.

The development of major commercial distilling in the Scottish Lowlands accelerated following the passing of the Gin Act in 1736, which imposed heavy excise duty on gin in an effort to curb drunkenness, while exempting whisky. However, Lowland whisky tended to be of poor quality, and much was actually exported to England to be rectified into gin.

The Coffey revolution

One of the most significant developments in the history of Scotch whisky was the creation of the continuous still, patented in 1827 by Robert Stein, and simplified and made more efficient by Aeneas Coffey, who patented his version in 1830.

The Coffey still allowed unmalted grain to be distilled into alcohol on a far larger scale than was possible in a traditional copper pot still, and the continuous nature of the process also contributed to the volumes that could be produced. Not only did the Coffey still turn out large quantities of comparatively cheap, high strength spirit, it was also extremely consistent, unlike that distilled in many Highland pot stills. Initially, much of the comparatively characterless spirit produced in Scotland's Coffey stills was exported to England for rectification into gin, as with some Lowland malt whisky, but mid-century legislation created the opportunity for a new form of Scotch whisky which would take the world by storm.

The 1860 Spirits Act allowed malt and grain whisky 'under bond' to be blended for the first time, opening the way for merchants such as Andrew Usher of Edinburgh effectively to create an entirely new drink. Blended Scotch whisky offered an easier drinking and more consistent alternative to pot still whisky, and in the hands of a group of buccaneering entrepreneurs such as James Buchanan, Tommy Dewar and Peter Mackie, blended Scotch became a global phenomenon.

Blends supreme

The story of Scotch continued to be dominated by blends through good times and bad during the 20th century, with significant expansion of distilling capacity taking place in the decades following World War II.

Single malts were something of a curiosity outside parts of the Scottish Highlands, with one notable exception being William Grant & Sons' Glenfiddich, which had first been exported in 1963 and established footholds in many overseas markets where it would dominate for decades to come.

Glenfiddich was not alone, however, in flying the flag for single malts, with fellow Speyside brands like Glenlivet, Glen Grant and Macallan, along with Glenmorangie, all establishing loyal followings. Many of these distilleries were independently owned, and investment was made in high quality marketing campaigns and an emphasis on traditional craftsmanship and the importance of individual single malt characteristics.

Provenance was emphasised, and for Scotch consumers, particularly younger ones, this all provided a welcome and enticing proposition by comparison to the constant price-cutting and clichéd Scottish imagery associated with many blends. As a result, as single malts grew in popularity, so standard blends became associated with an ageing consumer profile, particularly in the UK.

One innovation that helped increase the popularity of single malts was the introduction in 1987 of The Classic Malts by DCL successor company to United Distillers. This comprised six single malts, chosen to represent different geographical regions of production, and the stylistic variations associated with them.

More recently, the world of Scotch whisky has seen a proliferation of new distillery development, much of it associated with the adventurous, experimental, microdistilling, provenance-rich sector of the market.

The gin craze

Parallel to the distillation of whisky in Scotland – and at times in England and Wales – gin-making has long been a second extremely important strand of the British spirits industry. Like whisky, the drink had its origins outside Britain, with the first records of gin production dating from Holland in the early 17th century, though other sources suggest it was being made in Italy prior to that time. Originally sold for medicinal purposes, gin was flavoured with juniper to give it a more attractive flavour, and the juniper contributed to its medicinal effectiveness.

During the Thirty Years' War in Europe (1618–48) British troops were given measures of gin – known as 'Dutch courage' – prior to engagement with the enemy, which led to a developing taste for it back in Britain. Distillation of gin went from something of a cottage industry to a major commercial enterprise, though the quality of the spirit was often far from high.

The arrival of King William III – 'William of Orange' – on the English throne in 1689 led to gin's greatest period of popularity, as he took a very positive attitude to the production of spirits. Anyone could distil gin on the basis of putting out a public announcement and waiting for ten days before commencing production. Soon gin consumption exceeded that of beer and ale, and workers would even be paid part of their wages in gin.

Distilling and retailing licences became compulsory in 1729, and a duty of two shillings per gallon was imposed on gin. This did nothing to reduce the amount of poor quality gin being consumed, however, and it is recorded that during 1730 London alone had more than 7,000 retail premises selling nothing but spirits.

Abuse of gin by the poor was now a major social problem, and one most famously recorded by William Hogarth in his 'Gin Lane' engravings, depicting a descent from propriety to insanity and death. It should be noted, however, that Hogarth was commissioned to create 'Gin Lane' by members of the brewing industry, keen to demonise the principal competition to their own products.

The establishment's response to what was sometimes known as 'The Gin Craze' was The Gin Act of 1736, which raised duty to £1 per gallon and the cost of a retailing licence to £50. The result was a dramatic rise in the cost of legally distilled gin, and widespread riots broke out when the Act was imposed.

The legislation was largely ignored by distillers, however, and in excess of 11m gallons of gin were produced in London each year during the late 1730s, which was said to account for 14 gallons per adult male! In the six years following The Gin Act, output rose by almost half, but only two new licences were applied for.

Respectability

Ultimately, The Gin Act was repealed in 1742, and distillers participated in drafting new legislation enacted as The Gin Act of 1751, which imposed fair levels of excise duty, relatively high retail prices and made licensed retailers answerable to local magistrates.

As a result, gin began to lose its reputation as 'mother's ruin,' and its new-found respectability led to the emergence of highly professional, responsible gin manufacturers, who ensured their spirits were of good quality. Alexander Gordon established his company to produce London Dry Gin in 1769, and Plymouth Gin was first distilled in 1793.

During the mid-19th century, gin was given a boost by the British in India, who adopted a local custom of using bark of the chinchona tree as a medicine against malaria, which contained quinine. To combat its extreme bitterness, gin, sugar and lime were added, along with ice, creating that enduring British staple the 'gin and tonic.'

The development of cocktails also gave gin even greater popularity, and the gin-based Martini is said to have been invented around 1888. A century later, cocktails returned to fashion after a lengthy lull, and a new generation of small-scale gin distilleries subsequently emerged, with many also producing craft vodkas, mirroring the increase in whisky microdistilling. Indeed, many of the new generation of gin and vodka distilleries also have longer term strategies to produce and market whisky.

Case study

Organic Distilleries
www.organicarchitects.co.uk

Organic Distilleries Ltd is a sister company to Organic Architects, which was established by architect Gareth Roberts in 2005. The company is based in Helensburgh, Argyll and Bute, Scotland, and operates as a specialist architecture and consultancy group for the worldwide design and delivery of distilleries.

Gareth was born in Macclesfield, Cheshire, but brought up in Callander, Perthshire, from the age of 12. He worked in the field of urban design and spent time in the United States and Russia before striking out on his own. "Initially we were building houses, but very alternative eco-developments that encouraged a sense of community," he explains. "We first got involved with distilleries three years later.

'Organic' means we're into the 'eco' side of things, including energy efficiency, but there's also the 'evolution' aspect. People come to us with the idea of a building, and we end of giving them the keys. We supply HMRC advice, specialist insurance advice – everything from a client saying 'I might want a distillery' through to spirit flowing."

The company's first distillery project was to design Ardnamurchan, remotely situated at Glenbeg on the Ardnamurchan peninsula, just north of the Isle of Mull on the west coast of Scotland. The distillery was built for independent whisky bottlers Adelphi Distillery Ltd and is powered by a biomass plant which makes it one of the most low-carbon distilleries in the world.

Gareth Roberts says that "Getting kerosene to such a remote location to fire the boiler was always going to be expensive, and they also wanted to use local fuel sources. They chop local timber and use it for bio-mass. If you can cut production costs per litre then that's obviously good for business, and bio-mass is also good for the environment."

He adds that "We put the stills in the windows at Ardnamurchan. Still necks need replacing quite often, and if you put the stills by windows you can vent beneath them, and take still parts out through the floor. There's a great aesthetic element to having the stills by windows, too, especially at night. The stills are the stars."

On the subject of distillery design, Gareth points out that "You have challenges to deal with such as the fact that a stillhouse is dry and hot, while mashing is a moist process, and both areas of the distillery need to be highly ventilated. You're constrained by building regulations and planning, health and safety and best practice legislation. We bring all of these factors together and what we create has to fit into the landscape, it's got to be attractive and look as though it suits the place.

"The distillery is your 'brand home,' so you want it to look and feel right. Authenticity is everything in the world we live in. People will soon migrate away from the brand if you're not authentic. The visitor aspect is very important. When you design from scratch rather than using an existing building you can give the distillery a great flow for visitors."

Since designing Ardnamurchan, Organic Distilleries has worked on two other now-completed Scottish distillery projects, namely Drimnin and Lindores. The former is even more remote in location than Ardnamurchan, and is best reached via the Isle of Mull rather than the mainland itself! Like Lindores, it was based on a former farm steading, and Gareth Roberts notes that "Drimnin works with a biomass boiler, the same as Ardnamurchan. Again, it's a very remote location with access issues and related high costs to get kerosene in, and again there are lots of local trees.

"My real interest is in terroir. As far as I'm concerned, the atmosphere in which whisky is matured is key though the prevailing weather is also important. I think microdistillers, the guys we work with, should be making more of this aspect. We've created traditional 'dunnage' warehouses at Ardnamurchan and Drimnin, and a byre conversion at Lindores is a dunnage warehouse. You need thick, heavy walls to help make for only small temperature changes. I like the idea of getting the character of the place into the whisky through dunnage."

When it comes to working with a historic site like Lindores in Fife, where the medieval abbey ruins stand opposite the distillery, an architect's sensitivity to the issues of merging old and new is essential. Gareth says that "We kept as much of the old material as we could. If you'd come along before we started on the distillery, you'd have seen three gables just like now, and we've used Fife pantile roofs and slates. It's an authentic local roof, rebuilt as it was previously, but there's a new steel structure in place under that.

"Two-thirds of the buildings are devoted to history and interpretation – there's lots of story to tell. You had historical precedent as well as just an old steading. We incorporated some pieces of columns and stones that were uncovered during construction and examined by archaeologists to give them a new lease of life. The distillery buildings face the abbey, look straight into it, so you have a real link between the old and the new. There was a strong brief at Lindores for us because of the heritage angle."

One of Organic Distilleries' most recent projects was to design Princetown distillery on Dartmoor. The site is owned by the Duchy of Cornwall, and Gareth explains that "It's a courtyard and a group of buildings, all served from the back, so the front is clear and uncluttered. You have a nice flow right through, from the stillhouse into the two-storey bonded warehouse. Building started in early 2018 and it will be online in a couple of years. We have to get approval from Prince Charles for each stage, and knowing he's a keen watercolourist we had the initial plans done with watercolours. It worked!

"Most of the people we work with want space to expand – leave room for more washbacks and more stills if necessary in the future. I tend to design 'courtyard' distilleries because they are easy to access and easy to expand."

While declaring that "Whisky-making in England is set to get much bigger, I think," Gareth points out that "We are also now designing many more small-scale gin distilleries. It's mainly about getting planning permission and advising people on sourcing kit. When it can be done in a kitchen there's not much actual architectural input! We can advise on all the rules and regulations.

"Whisky has a mystique that can add value, but things can go wrong – there's no guarantee that after spending time maturing in a cask the end product will be good. It costs a minimum of £2 million to get a basic whisky distillery up and running, but it's amazing with gin distilling just how little you need to make it. Tens of thousands of pounds, maybe. You could even build a distillery in a shipping container: I'd love to do that!"

Noting that "You can start with a 50-litre still, almost experimental size," Gareth observes that "It's quite anti-globalist, and I'm sure that's where the future is for some people. Microdistilling is a lifestyle choice for many, and the rise of the internet and social media have helped tremendously. Microdistilling is the 'sexy' end of distilling – you can have some fun with it. For me, it's all about localism. Whether its cheese, whisky or botanicals for gin, it's all about terroir, and there are not many products for which that's true. It's great to see opportunities for sustainable local enterprise. Keeping it real is crucial. Authenticity is the key."

The structure of the spirit industry in the UK

Overview

According to the wine and Spirit Trade Association (WSTA), in 2015 the spirits industry in the UK generated £28.2bn in economic activity and £9.8bn in sales. Taking into account duty, VAT, Corporation Tax and income tax, it contributed £6.9bn to the public purse.

The industry was worth £4bn to shops and supermarkets, and £5.8bn to bars, pubs and restaurants. In terms of exports, 1.25bn litres of spirits were sent overseas from the UK, with whisky accounting for 1.2bn bottles, gin for 204m bottles, and vodka for 54m bottles. Around 186,000 people were directly employed in the spirits industry, with a further 110,000 employed in the supply-chain.

Whisky

Inevitably, a high percentage of the above values were generated by a relatively small number of large-scale producers, with the Diageo-owned Johnnie Walker portfolio of blended Scotch whiskies accounting for volume sales of 17.4 m nine-litre cases worldwide in 2016, giving it a global Scotch whisky market share of 21.5 per cent. Diageo boasted a total malt whisky distillation capacity of 121.3m litres of spirit in 2016, accounting for 31.7 per cent of the market, followed by Pernod Ricard with 17.1 per cent.

Diageo's J&B featured at number five in the best-selling Scotch blends list, while places two and three were occupied respectively by Pernod Ricard's Ballantine's and Chivas Regal respectively. The Scotch whisky industry's third largest distiller in terms of capacity, William Grant & Sons Ltd, took fourth place with its portfolio of blends, headed by Family Reserve.

A notable feature of the Scotch whisky scene in recent years has been the growth in popularity of single malts, and the share of revenue earned by malts as a total of Scotch whisky exports has grown to 26 per cent, hitting the £1bn mark for the first time in 2016. Grant's Glenfiddich and Pernod Ricard's The Glenlivet fight it out for supremacy among the single malts, each with a market share around the 12 per cent mark in recent years.

Gin

In terms of gin, in 2016 the UK exported a record £474m worth of gin, up 12 per cent on the previous year, and worth £53m more than the previous year. In 2015 a total of 139 countries bought British gin.

Since 2012, the value of British gin exports has grown by 32 per cent, adding the equivalent value of £227m in just five years, while volume sales have also risen by 36 per cent. A remarkable 44 new gin distilleries opened in 2016, with 100 new licences issued during the past two years.

Five British-distilled gins feature in the global 'top ten' of brands, headed by perennial favourite Gordon's, which sold 4.62m nine litre cases in 2016 for owner Diageo. Second place fell to Bacardi's Bombay Sapphire (3.05m cases in 2016), distilled in Hampshire, while Diageo's dominance of the world gin markets is emphasised by its Tanqueray brand occupying third place, selling 2.9m cases. Both Gordon's and Tanqueray are distilled in Diageo's vast Cameronbridge complex in Fife, Scotland.

Diageo's most potent rival Pernod Ricard is not left out of the gin equation, taking fourth place with Beefeater (2.7m cases), distilled in London. William Grant & Sons Ltd also thrive in the gin market, courtesy of its idiosyncratic Hendrick's expression: a relative newcomer being launched in 1999. It accounted for 953,361 cases in 2016, recording significant growth on its 2015 performance of 788,823 cases.

Vodka

Only one of the world's top ten vodkas is produced in the UK, and the brand is also distilled in several other countries. The vodka in question is Smirnoff, owned by Diageo, and in 2016 it sold a total of 25.5m nine litre cases. In the UK, Smirnoff is made at Diageo's Cameronbridge distilling complex in Fife. The second biggest global vodka seller is Absolut, distilled in Sweden, but owned by Diageo's arch competitor Pernod Ricard.

It should be borne in mind that while companies such as Diageo, Pernod Ricard, Bacardi and William Grant are key players in the UK spirits' industry, they also operate on a global basis, and their British plants and brands only account for part of their activities.

Taking an overall view of the UK spirits market, the WSTA noted the number of distilleries in operation during 2015. Of the 233 registered UK distilleries, 119 were in Scotland, 11 in Northern Ireland, 12 in Wales and 91 in England. That year saw the creation of 12 new distilleries in Scotland, ten in Northern Ireland, six in Wales and 28 in England, illustrating the dynamism behind

behind the UK spirits sector. A significant number of the new distilleries developed during and since 2015 fall into the microdistillery classification.

The history of modern microdistilling

Influence of brewing

The global microdistilling movement has at its heart a reaction to the apparently increasingly homogenised offerings provided by a relatively small number of international companies, much like the microbrewing movement that preceded it, and continues to thrive.

US microbrewing followed the lead of the British 'Real Ale' revival, spearheaded by The Campaign for Real Ale (CAMRA), which was established in 1971. The first 'real ale' brewer in the USA was probably homebrewer Jack McAuliffe, who opened his New Albion Brewing Company in Somona County, California, in 1976. Around that time, there were fewer than 100 breweries in operation across the whole of the USA, but at the close of 2016, that figure stood at a record of just over 5,000. Similarly, in the UK brewery numbers have increased to more than 2,000, a figure last seen in the 1920s.

A significant number of US microbrewers began to expand into distillation, and other producers joined the party, with many states relaxing stringent regulations that had prevented the creation of new distilling enterprises – particularly those small in scale – since the era of Prohibition (1920–33).

In New York State, for example, 2002 saw the introduction of relatively inexpensive licensing permits for 'small batch' distilleries, with the codicil that at least 50 per cent of ingredients used in distillation were sourced from New York farms.

By late 2016 the total of licenced microdistilleries in the States was in excess of 1,300, and UK microdistilling has also expanded dramatically, rising to more than 270 operations by late 2016. This has been in part due to the growing desire to produce spirits on an artisan scale, opting for originality and experimentation over conformity and scale, but also because of the fact that UK authorities, like those across the Atlantic, have come to take an altogether more positive attitude to microdistilling.

Licensing

It is often stated that London distiller Sipsmith was responsible for creating the legal environment whereby microdistilling could thrive by successfully lobbying HMRC for a licence for a still of less than 1,800 litres in 2009. However, Loch Ewe distillery in the north-west Highlands of Scotland had been granted a licence for two 120 litre whisky stills six years earlier, on the basis that a loophole existed in the regulations.

Once the licence was granted, the loophole was duly closed, though study of HMRC's regulations relating to the licensing of stills reveals that the figure of 1,800 litres was never set in stone, and the body declares that "We may consider licence applications in respect of stills below 18 hectolitres [1,800 litres] where there are satisfactory controls in place to protect the revenue and the required control resources are not disproportionate to the amount of revenue involved."

Geographical diversity

One significant effect of the growth of microdistilling in the UK is the remarkable geographical diversity that has ensued. Distilling now takes place from Shetland in the north to the Isle of Wight in the south, and whisky has broken away from its traditional home of Scotland to be produced in a range of locations south of the border, including Devon, Norfolk, Suffolk, Gloucestershire, Yorkshire, Cumbria and West Wales. Indeed, whisky distilling returned to London in 2013 courtesy of The London Distillery Company for the first time since the closure of Lea Valley distillery in 1908.

Not only is there geographical diversity, there is also a great deal of product diversity, with the very nature of microdistilling being ideally suited to limited editions, short runs and a degree of experimentation not easily undertaken by larger, volume-led operators.

Diverse distillations – whisky

In terms of whisky, to qualify as 'Scotch,' spirit must meet stringent criteria in terms of ingredients, processing and maturation, and the EU definition of whisk(e)y specifies a minimum maturation period of three years and a minimum strength of 40% ABV. However, even in Scotland, a number of microdistillers have made it clear that they will follow their own path and not necessarily produce 'Scotch' whisky. Indeed, some of their offerings may well have to be labelled as 'Spirit Drink.'

One such distillery is Lone Wolf, at Alford in Aberdeenshire, and the distilling arm of brewing rebels BrewDog. Using American pale ale yeast, Lone Wolf has distilled quantities of spirit from 70 per cent malted rye with 30 per cent Maris Otter barley, and 60 per cent malted wheat with 40 per cent Maris Otter barley. Wash is supplied by the adjacent brewhouse, and Lone Wolf's distillers plan to experiment with crystal, chocolate and roasted malts, as well as lager yeast.

Also in Aberdeenshire, Twin River distillery – an offshoot of Deeside Brewery – works with a mix of brewing yeast and distillers' yeast, with wash from its 80 Shillings beer recipe, using principally pale malt, with some chocolate malt. Like Lone Wolf, Twin River has produced rye whisky, a move already made by Arbikie in Angus. Larger-scale Scottish distillers such as Bruichladdich on Islay and Inchdairnie in Fife have also produced ryes, with the Inchdairnie distillers pointing out that historically, Scotch whisky was often made using rye grain, and their 'innovation' is actually the restoration of a practice widely employed a century ago.

Many start-up distillers opt to begin by making white spirits such as gin and vodka, as these will provide a relatively quick source of income, while – as already noted – whisky must be matured for three years to qualify as such.

Gin

In terms of gins, producers tend to focus on non-core sourcing botanicals on a local basis to create a 'USP.' So it is, for example, that Dunnet Bay Distillers use rose root and sea buckthorn berries, native to the Caithness coast in their Rock Rose Gin, and Tarquin Ledbetter of Cornwall employs home-grown Devon violets in his Tarquin's Gin.

Apart from botanicals, some of the new wave of gin makers have also created 'Navy Strength' gins, more recently the preserve only of the Plymouth Gin brand. Navy strength gin harks back to the days when the Royal Navy feared it was being supplied with watered-down gin, and used to test its strength by pouring a small quantity onto gunpowder – usually stowed below decks close to the stores. If the gunpowder failed to ignite, the gin was less than 114 proof, or 57% ABV, the strength now attributed to 'navy strength' gin.

However flavoured gins have also become popular, with Sacred of London producing Grapefruit Gin and Liquorice Gin, for example, while J J Whitley offers a Nettle Gin. Rhubarb gin has also become

Case study

Dyfi Distillery
www.dyfidistillery.com

Dyfi distillery is located in the former slate mining village of Corris in Mid-Wales, and the area has the distinction of being a UNESCO Biosphere – the only one in the country. It is home to some of the most diverse flora, cleanest water, darkest skies and lowest population in Europe.

Here brothers Pete and Danny Cameron and their families produce gin, with Danny explaining that "Our primary interest is making gin with a sense of place, and to achieve that around 70 per cent of the botanicals we use are foraged within the UNESCO World Biosphere Reserve where we are located."

Using foraged botanicals means that not every batch of Dyfi gin is absolutely identical, but as Danny Cameron says, "If we need to sacrifice a small degree of consistency in exchange for absolute quality, I think our customers understand that. But equally, we use preservation of foraged botanicals to allow us to repeat botanical quantities between batches of each gin, and our foraging is mostly site specific.

"So, we have processes to help mitigate variation, but we are dealing with natural ingredients. Even for non-foraged ingredients, we only use fresh lemon peel for example, so there is some variation in sourcing organic unwaxed lemons in a location as remote as ours, but we prefer the brightness this delivers, and value that above the greater consistency that dried peel might provide."

Dyfi distillery is part of a craft centre comprising nine units and opened in 2016, with Danny Cameron noting that "We self-funded, with assistance of a small grant from the Welsh Government's Food Business Investment Scheme."

Explaining how he and Pete came to be running a distillery in Mid-Wales, Danny Cameron says that "I started in the restaurant trade and found myself writing my first wine list while still doing a hotel school internship. I was subsequently a head sommelier, restaurateu and hotel manager before becoming a wine merchant, and then involved in importing, consultancy, and generic promotion in the wine trade. I still judge at the Decanter World Wine Awards, and in 2015 was very honoured to be made a Commander of the

Order of Prince Henry by the Portuguese President for services to that country's' wine industry.

"My brother Pete moved to Dyfi after leaving school to study Environmental Biology and forgot to leave. He has foraged, kept bees and hill farmed in this valley ever since. When we were discussing ideas to produce something in this special place with genuine provenance, a foraged-led gin seemed the natural thing to do. That, or make cheese."

When it came to equipping the distillery, two 100-litre stills were acquired from the Colorado company Mile Hi Stills, with Danny Cameron noting that "We were setting up on a fairly tight budget but wanted to use equipment which was highly adaptable. We also further modified the stills on arrival here. One of our first visitors, who is also a distiller, asked how we worked, and we explained about our botanical preparations and calibration, the use of two small stills so we could make every decision genuinely evidence-based by monitoring variables accurately and our methodology of adapting our stills. He said, "this is the nearest thing I've seen to precision-distilling," so we started to use the term.

"We are now having a new still made very precisely to order for us by Muller in the Black Forest, Germany. It will be a consolidation of all we have learned in the last few years, which is why we didn't do this when we started. The Mile Hi stills have been brilliant for their adaptability and indeed quality of distillate, but we want to try to achieve a couple of things with a new still. These are to seek continuous improvement in what we do and to slightly increase our batch size, though the idea here is to allow us to have one or two days off, rather than scale production up very much!"

As well as distillation equipment, Danny Cameron is keen to emphasise the importance of packaging, saying that "The packaging should be a direct reflection of the amount of effort put into the product, and the values of the producer. If the packaging is cheap, the consumer has every reason to believe the contents will be mediocre. If the packaging is glossy and shiny, the consumer has every reason to believe the contents have been heavily processed, too.

"We worked with a brilliant small design team called Dare! who I knew from their work in the wine trade. But I think it's important that the producer brings their own ideas to the table. I'm sure Simon and Debbie at Dare! used a lot of very naughty words whenever I came off the phone to them but were always patient and meticulous. I still have my original drawing of our snail and bee logo (to represent Hibernation and Pollination) which I held up to them to see during an early Skype call. It perfectly demonstrates why you need creative people to turn any design ideas into a gorgeous reality."

In terms of products, Dyfi Original Gin remains a firm favourite, and is a classic London dry gin, produced in 200 bottle batches, bottled at 45% ABV and each bottle is vintage-dated with the distilling season, batch-numbered and signed.

Additionally, the distillery makes seasonal Pollination and Hibernation expressions. As Danny Cameron explains, "On a canvas of carefully selected classic gin botanicals, we 'paint' the flavours only Dyfi can combine, including wild flowers, aromatic leaves, fruits and conifer tips. The botanicals we forage for Hibernation Gin are influenced by the later season and include wild crab apples, blackberries, bilberries and lingonberries."

Hibernation has the distinction of being the only gin to be aged in a fully-seasoned white port barrel, and Cameron says that "We feel that barrel ageing should always be done to improve something, rather than just change it for its own sake, and this should mean creating a unique formulation. And if only using one very specific type of barrel, we should create a botanical bill which is specific to that barrel character. For example, our botanical bill for this gin includes wild crab apples, which in the new make distillate gives a bit of harshness, but after the ageing actually adds to the freshness of the finished gin, as well as marrying with the barrel character wonderfully."

notably fashionable, with Warner Edwards in Northamptonshire producing 4,000 bottles of Victoria's Rhubarb Gin during 2014, and in excess of 350,000 bottles in 2014.

Vodka

When it comes to vodka, potatoes are employed by a number of distillers, including Chase of Herefordshire and Arbikie in Angus, with Chase also selling Marmalade Vodka, Lemon Marmalade Vodka, Rhubarb Vodka and English Smoked Oak Vodka.

Meanwhile, Dunnet Bay Distillers add Holy Grass, found by the River Thurso, to their vodka, along with an infusion of apples and apple juice. Flavoured vodkas, like flavoured gins, are growing in availability, with The English Spirit Distillery at Dullingham in Cambridgeshire marketing Toffee Vodka, and Arbikie in Angus producing a seasonal fresh strawberry vodka. More left-field is Arbikie's Chilli Vodka, and Pure Milk Vodka made by Black Cow distillery in Dorset from fermented whey, which is triple distilled.

Greater diversity

Whisky, gin and vodka may be the most common produce of British microdistillers, but some firms have cast their nets wider in search of the more exotic. The Sacred Spirits Company makes a variety of English vermouths, while north of the border Great British Vermouth produces Dry Vermod Vermouth near Edinburgh.

The English Spirit Distillery also distils English Sambuca, using anise and elderflower eau-de-vie. Additionally, the company offers Old Salt Rum, produced at its distillery from molasses and raw sugar cane. Another rare distiller of British rum is Dark Matter distillery at Banchory in Aberdeenshire – the first rum distillery in Scotland. That most French of spirits, pastis, has also been claimed by British microdistillers, with Tarquin's Cornish Pastis being an aniseed and fennel aperitif with the addition of Cornish gorse flowers.

Existing businesses – agriculture and brewing

While many microdistilling projects have been started from scratch, some have been add-ons to existing businesses, most notably agricultural and brewing enterprises. Ludlow Vineyard, located on the lower slopes of Brown Clee Hill in Shropshire, boasts 10 acres of vineyards containing some 8,000 vines, along with apple orchards. The installation of a still means that the Vineyard has now diversified into the production of 'Shropshire Applejack' apple brandy, pear, apple, damson and greengage eau-de-vie, and a range of fruit liqueurs.

Long before Ludlow Vineyard moved into distillation, Julian Temperley of Pass Vale Farm, home to 180 acres of cider apple orchards at Burrow Hill in Somerset, was distilling cider brandy. Indeed, in 1989, Temperley was at the forefront of British microdistilling, being granted the UK's first cider distilling licence, and today half of the cider produced is distilled in a pair of copper stills, named Josephine and Fifi, in recognition of their French origins. Somerset cider brandy is now sold at 3, 5, 10, 15 and 20 years, while liqueurs and Somerset Pomona – a blend of apples and cider brandy - are also on offer.

Away from the world of apples and cider, other farming enterprises have taken to distilling, utilising their own crops, including potatoes. Arbikie Highland Estate is located near the North Sea coast of Angus, between Dundee and Aberdeen, and four generations of the Stirling family have farmed there. Potatoes grown on the 2,000 acres have been distilled into vodka since 2014, with gin and whisky following the year after, with the latter being produced from home-grown barley.

Another farming venture with potatoes at its heart is Chase Distillery, in Herefordshire. There William Chase and his family have been distilling since 2008, having previously established the Tyrrells crisps brand, which Chase sold for £300m. From an initial annual turnover of £140,000, Chase was selling 10,000 bottles of spirits per week, with export markets in 36 countries, during early 2016. As Britain's first 'single estate' distillery, Chase grows all potatoes used in the production of its spirits on site, utilising specialist potato varieties to make a premium vodka.

Brewing

Given that the initial processes of brewing beer and distilling spirits are almost identical, it is not surprising that several UK beer-makers have also diversified into distillation. First to do so was Adnams, based at Southwold in Suffolk and operating on a site where beer has been made since 1345. In 2010 the Copper House Distillery was created within Adnams' Sole Bay Brewery, and 'wash' made from the same locally-grown barley, wheat, rye or oats is used in the production of gin, vodka and whisky as is used to make beers such as Ghost Ship pale ale and Broadside premium bitter.

Another long-established brewer, St Austell of Cornwall, founded in 1851 by Walter Hicks, has followed Adnams' example, creating wash from Cornish-grown Maris Otter barley, which is then double distilled at Healey's Cyder Farm in a tiny 1,200 litres traditional copper pot still. The initial result was Hicks & Healey Cornish Single Malt Seven Years Old Whiskey – the first whisk(e)y made in Cornwall for around 300 years.

In East Yorkshire, the Mellor family of Wold Top Brewery near Hunmanby, created a stand-alone distilling enterprise not far from their farm during 2015/16, in partnership with long-standing friend David Thompson. Using brewery wash, they now produce the first ever Yorkshire single malt whisky.

In Scotland, BrewDog at Ellon in Aberdeenshire has established Lone Wolf Spirits (see p.14), to produce gin, vodka and a wide range of experimental whiskies, while in the same county, The Deeside Brewery has set up Twin River Distillery, with the intention of being equally experimental.

Born in the Borders brewery near Jedburgh is another beer-making operation that has moved into microdistilling, starting to produce Lilliard Gin in 2017 after a successful crowd-funding venture. Based in a converted cowshed, this was the first distillery to operate in the Scottish Borders since 1837, and the first ever gin distillery. Born in the Borders started out in 2011 as a farming diversification project, complete with 'plough to pint' ethos, using home-grown barley.

Getting in on the act

Given the success of microbreweries, and the desire by a significant section of the beer-drinking public to consume relatively local brews with genuine provenance, it is hardly surprising that a number of major brewers have bought up small-scale operations, running them at arm's length.

In 2015, Anheuser-Busch InBev purchased London's Camden Town Brewery, and in the same year the world's second-largest brewer SABMiller acquired Meantime Brewing Company, though by then Meantime was hardly a microbrewer anymore, having expanded to operate a 120,000-hectolitre modern brew plant.

SABMiller's ownership of Meantime was short-lived in any case, as a regulatory condition of Anheuser-Busch InBev's takeover of SABMiller in 2016 was the sale of the Greenwich operation, and Meantime subsequently was bought by Asahi Breweries of Japan in October 2016.

Distillers

Inevitably, the world of distilling has mirrored that of brewing, with Britain's largest independent, family-owned distiller William Grant & Sons Ltd being first to invest in microdistilling – when it acquired the Hudson whiskey brands of New York State's Tuthilltown Spirits in 2010. Such was the success of its foray into craft distillation that 2017 saw Grant's buy up the distillery itself.

Fellow independent Scotch whisky-maker Ian Macleod Distillers purchased Spencerfield Spirits during 2016, principally in order to own the increasingly successful and award-winning small-batch Edinburgh Gin brand, established by former whisky industry executive Alex Nicol and his wife Jane in 2010.

Altogether more international was the 2016 acquisition of London's Sipsmith by the world's third largest distiller, Beam Suntory Inc of the USA for a price in the region of £50m. Beam Suntory is responsible for such leading brands as Jim Beam, Laphroaig and Bowmore whiskies, Courvoisier cognac and Gilbey's Ggn, and Sipsmith had demonstrated significant global growth in terms of sales since its establishment in 2009. The firm was exporting 30 per cent of its output at the time of its sale to Beam Suntory, with the US being a particularly strong market.

It is not only British small-scale distilling ventures that are being bought up by major companies, as Pernod Ricard – second only to Diageo in the international drinks business – acquired German dry gin brand Monkey 47 early in 2016.

Useful organisations

As microdistilling enterprises have proliferated, so a number of organisations have been created to help distillers make the best decisions possible, offering advice and keeping them up to date with legislative changes. Principal among these is:

The British Distillers Alliance

or BDA, **www.britishdistillersalliance.com**, a non-profit making body that provides a professional service for independent and craft businesses in the spirits production industry and supply chain. The BDA represents distillers, rectifiers and compounders and those in related sectors.

According to the organisation:

- The BDA will principally deliver information at a detailed operational level suitable for the day-to-day needs of small and new businesses.

- We will respond to government consultations and seek to influence government policy. We will also raise matters on our own initiative.
- We will initiate seminars for members with HMRC to discuss policy and operational matters in our sector. We provide advice on all relevant compliance matters and will advise on industry best practice and training.

In 2014, The Scottish Craft Distillers Association **www.scottishdistillers.online** was formed, comprising new and emerging Scottish distillers and Scottish academics. The SCDA was created after members of Interface Food & Drink's Craft Distillers Common Interest Group (CIG) decided that an organisation was required to represent their collective needs. The CIG then formed the new association in partnership with Strathearn Distilleries and the International Centre for Brewing & Distilling. In 2018 the association was renamed The Scottish Distillers Association.

The objects of the Scottish Distillers Association are:

- **Promotion:** Promoting collaboratively the products and services of the members of the Scottish Distillers Association.
- **Representation:** Providing unified trade representation for Scottish craft distillers at political, legislative and environmental levels.
- **Innovation:** Innovating technical solutions and supply chain improvements to increase the production and supply of quality spirits from Scottish craft distillers.
- **Market Development:** Identifying new UK and export markets for the products and services of the members of the Scottish Craft Distillers Association.
- **Accreditation:** Developing a trade marque or similar, including all related intellectual property rights, to accredit members' products.
- **Common Interest Grouping:** Engaging with research, academia, skills development or knowledge transfer to enhance the value of the Association's work or its members' property or undertakings.

Craft Distilling Expo

www.distillingexpo.com staged in London each October, comprises a series of events revolving around a distilling trade show. There are whisky and gin distilling workshops and a toughly-contested Gin of the Year competition, where craft gins are judged in seven categories.

In 2017, the main Expo featured over 30 vendors of distiller supplies

– including still manufacturers and bottle and closure suppliers, all staged within the premises of what was once one of London's greatest breweries, namely the Old Truman Brewery in Brick Lane.

The Craft Distilling Expo also marks the launch of the annual Crafdi Directory of European Distilleries, which now boasts over 360 entries from across Europe. In addition to location and website information, each entry now includes details of what spirits are made at the distilleries in question making it a notably valuable resource for distillers and aficionados alike.

The Gin Guild

www.theginguild.com

The Gin Guild was incorporated by the Worshipful Company of Distillers, one of London's traditional Livery Companies, incorporated by Royal Charter in 1638. The historical role of the Worshipful Company of Distillers was to hold key responsibilities for the control and regulation of early gin distillers.

According to the Guild, "The Worshipful Company of Distillers aims, via the work of the Gin Guild, to be at the heart of the distilling industry to provide and facilitate a wider opportunity for those involved in the gin industry, allowing them to participate in a modern convivial industry forum, whilst reflecting and including many of the traditions of the City of London."

There are various classes of membership:
- Founder Wardens, appointed by each of the four founding companies.
- Wardens, including distillers and brand owners.
- Rectifiers, made up of others involved in the wider gin industry including leading bartenders, spirits journalists and educators as well as those working in production and distribution.

The Gin Guild hosts an annual 'Ginposium' – the industry's annual seminar, when some of the world's most respected personalities and experts from the drinks and gin trade gather to discuss the state of the gin industry and share their knowledge and expertise on all things gin.

The Institute of Brewing and Distilling

www.ibd.org.uk

The Institute of Brewing & Distilling (IBD) is the world's leading professional body for people working in brewing and distilling.

As an international professional and educational body, the IBD promotes "The advancement of the education and professional development in the science and technology of brewing, distilling and related industries."

Dating back to 1886, the IBD now boasts over 5,000 members and is the largest global professional body for brewers and distillers, and the only one with a worldwide footprint. Global membership is administered on a geographic basis with sections around the world.

The IBD offers a range of examinations and qualifications in brewing, distilling, malting and packaging, ranging from the Fundamentals of Brewing and Packaging and of Distilling for nontechnical personnel, through General Certificates in Brewing, Distilling, Malting or Packaging, to Diplomas in Brewing, Distilling or Packaging. The ultimate accolade is the Master Brewer or Distiller qualification, which assesses levels of both competence and knowledge in the technical management of the production process.

Supporting its members through lectures, technical visits, seminars and conferences worldwide, the IBD also publishes the monthly Brewer and Distiller International magazine and quarterly Journal of the Institute of Brewing.

The Scotch Whisky Association
www.scotch-whisky.org.uk

The Scotch Whisky Association's (SWA) role is to advance the global interests and profile of Scotch whisky, its members and of the industry as a whole. The SWA states that "By building strong relationships with all levels of government and opinion-formers and by making a visible impact on public debate we will:

- Be a trusted voice in the debate on alcohol and society.
- Support a competitive, sustainable and fairly
  taxed industry.
- Safeguard the Scotch whisky category.
- Ensure fair access to all markets worldwide.

"We see the Scotch whisky industry as a significant Scottish and British economic and cultural asset that boosts growth and jobs, that strongly supports the communities with which we work and that combines the very best of the traditional and the modern."

The SWA can trace its origins back to October 1912. The original organisation, the Wine & Spirit Brand Association changed its name to the Whisky Association in 1917, and this in turn became the SWA in 1940.

The Wine and Spirit Trade Association
www.wsta.co.uk

The Wine and Spirit Trade Association (WSTA) represents over 300 companies producing, importing, exporting, transporting and selling wines and spirits in the United Kingdom. Members range from major retailers, brand owners and wholesalers to fine wine and spirit specialists, logistics and bottling companies.

According to the WSTA, "We campaign for a vibrant and sustainable wine and spirit industry, helping to build a future in which alcohol is produced, sold and enjoyed responsibly. Our policy work is extensive, on a wide range of social, regulatory and technical issues. The wine and spirit industry is eager to play its part in the UK's economic growth and we aim to shape an environment in which our sector can increase investment and remain competitive.

"Regulation is one of the biggest barriers to growth any business can face. We strive to ensure that regulation – whether at an international, national or local level – does not threaten the sector's viability. Another key part of building a sustainable future for the industry is fostering a culture in which our products are enjoyed responsibly. We are committed to working in partnership with the UK Government and other stakeholders to deliver this."

Key Issues addressed by the WSTA include alcohol taxation policy, alcohol pricing, public health and social responsibility, regulation of wine and spirit products, licencing laws, environment and sustainability, facilitating market access and distance selling, tackling fraud, logistics and customs and excise policy.

Chapter Two
The equipment needed and setting up

I n this chapter we focus on definitions of spirits, ingredients, the role of consultants, the equipment required to set up your distillery, environmental responsibilities and opportunities for training.

Definitions

The Scotch Whisky Regulations 2009 (SWR) set out precise definitions of the different types of Scotch whisky, and the wording that is legally acceptable in association with them.

- 2.1 Regulation 3 (2) contains the definitions of the different categories of Scotch Whisky: Single Malt, Single Grain, Blended Scotch Whisky, Blended Malt Scotch Whisky, Blended Grain Scotch Whisky.
- 2.2 The two basic types of Scotch Whisky, from which all blends are made, are Single Malt Scotch Whisky and Single Grain Scotch Whisky. In practice there is no change in the way that Single Malt Scotch Whisky and Single Grain Scotch Whisky must be produced.
- 2.3 Single Malt Scotch Whisky means a Scotch whisky produced from only water and malted barley at a single distillery by batch distillation in pot stills.
- 2.4 Single Grain Scotch Whisky means a Scotch whisky distilled at a single distillery but which, in addition to water and unmalted barley, may also be produced from whole grains or other malted or unmalted cereal. Excluded from the definition of "Single Grain Scotch Whisky" is any spirit which qualifies as a Single Malt Scotch Whisky or as a Blended Scotch whisky. The latter exclusion is to ensure that a Blended Scotch Whisky produced from single malt(s) and single grain(s) distilled at the same distillery does not also qualify as Single Grain Scotch Whisky.
- 2.5 The definition of Blended Scotch Whisky does change the existing law, but reflects traditional and current practice. Before the SWR, any combination of Scotch whiskies qualified as a Blended Scotch Whisky, including for example a blend of Single Malt Scotch Whiskies. However, Blended Malt Scotch Whisky is defined under the SWR as a combination of one or more Single Malt Scotch Whiskies with one or more Single Grain Scotch Whiskies, which accords with traditional practice.
- 2.6 Blended Malt Scotch Whisky means a blend of two or more single malt Scotch whiskies from different distilleries.

- 2.7 Blended Grain Scotch Whisky means a blend of two or more single grain Scotch whiskies from different distilleries.

In addition to the above basic definitions, there are many other criteria to bear in mind, relating to maturation, labelling, use of distillery names and geographical indicators – see **www.scotch-whisky.org** for full details.

Spirits are defined by Regulation (EC) No 110/2008 of the European Parliament and of the Council of 15 January 2008 on the definition, description, presentation, labelling and the protection of geographical indications of spirit drinks.

Definitions for categories of spirit drinks include the following:

Whisky or whiskey

(a) Whisky or whiskey is a spirit drink produced exclusively by:
  (i) distillation of a mash made from malted cereals with or without whole grains of other cereals, which has been:
    – saccharified by the diastase of the malt contained therein,
    – fermented by the action of yeast;
  (ii) one or more distillations at less than 94.8 % vol., so that the distillate has an aroma and taste derived from the raw materials used,
  (iii) maturation of the final distillate for at least three years in wooden casks not exceeding 700 litres capacity. The final distillate, to which only water and plain caramel (for colouring) may be added, retains its colour, aroma and taste derived from the production process referred to in points (i), (ii) and (iii).
(b) The minimum alcoholic strength by volume of whisky or whiskey shall be 40%.
(c) No addition of alcohol, diluted or not, shall take place.
(d) Whisky or whiskey shall not be sweetened or flavoured, nor contain any additives other than plain caramel used for colouring.

Grain spirit

(a) Grain spirit is a spirit drink produced exclusively by the distillation of a fermented mash of whole grain cereals and having organoleptic characteristics derived from the raw materials used.
(b) With the exception of 'Korn', the minimum alcoholic strength

by volume of grain spirit shall be 35%.

(c) No addition of alcohol, diluted or not, shall take place.

(d) Grain spirit shall not be flavoured.

(e) Grain spirit may only contain added caramel as a means to adapt colour.

(f) For a grain spirit to bear the sales denomination 'grain brandy', it must have been obtained by distillation at less than 95% vol. from a fermented mash of whole grain cereals, presenting organoleptic features deriving from the raw materials used.

Brandy

(a) Brandy is a spirit drink:

(i) produced from wine spirit, whether or not wine distillate has been added, distilled at less than 94.8 % vol., provided that that distillate does not exceed a maximum of 50% of the alcoholic content of the finished product,

(ii) matured for at least one year in oak receptacles or for at least six months in oak casks with a capacity of less than 1,000 litres,

(iii) containing a quantity of volatile substances equal to or exceeding 125 grams per hectolitre of 100% vol. alcohol, and derived exclusively from the distillation or redistillation of the raw materials used,

(iv) having a maximum methanol content of 200 grams per hectolitre of 100% vol. alcohol.

(b) The minimum alcoholic strength by volume of brandy shall be 36%.

(c) No addition of alcohol, diluted or not, shall take place.

(d) Brandy shall not be flavoured. This shall not exclude traditional production methods.

(e) Brandy may only contain added caramel as a means to adapt colour.

Cider spirit and perry spirit

(a) Cider spirit and perry spirit are spirit drinks:

(i) produced exclusively by the distillation at less than 86% vol. of cider or perry so that the distillate has an aroma and taste derived from the fruits,

(ii) having a quantity of volatile substances equal to or exceeding 200 grams per hectolitre of 100% vol. alcohol,

(iii) having a maximum methanol content of 1,000 grams

per hectolitre of 100% vol. alcohol.

(b) The minimum alcoholic strength by volume of cider spirit and of perry spirit shall be 37.5 %.

(c) No addition of alcohol, diluted or not, shall take place.

(d) Neither cider spirit nor perry spirit shall be flavoured.

(e) Cider spirit and perry spirit may only contain added caramel as a means to adapt colour.

Vodka

(a) Vodka is a spirit drink produced from ethyl alcohol of agricultural origin obtained following fermentation with yeast from either:

   (i) potatoes and/or cereals, or

   (ii) other agricultural raw materials,

distilled and/or rectified so that the organoleptic characteristics of the raw materials used and by-products formed in fermentation are selectively reduced.

This process may be followed by redistillation and/or treatment with appropriate processing aids, including treatment with activated charcoal to give it special organoleptic characteristics.

Maximum levels of residue for ethyl alcohol of agricultural origin shall meet those laid down in Annex I, except that the methanol content shall not exceed 10 grams per hectolitre of 100% vol. alcohol.

(b) The minimum alcoholic strength by volume of vodka shall be 37.5 %.

(c) The only flavourings that may be added are natural flavouring compounds present in distillate obtained from the fermented raw materials. In addition, the product may be given special organoleptic characteristics other than a predominant flavour.

d) The description, presentation or labelling of vodka not produced exclusively from the raw material(s) listed in paragraph (a)(i) shall bear the indication 'produced from ...', supplemented by the name of the raw material(s) used to produce the ethyl alcohol of agricultural origin.

Flavoured vodka

(a) Flavoured vodka is vodka which has been given a predominant flavour other than that of the raw materials.

(b) The minimum alcoholic strength by volume of flavoured vodka shall be 37.5 %.

(c) Flavoured vodka may be sweetened, blended, flavoured, matured or coloured.

(d) Flavoured vodka may also be sold under the name of any predominant flavour with the word 'vodka'.

Gin

(a) Gin is a juniper-flavoured spirit drink produced by flavouring organoleptically suitable ethyl alcohol of agricultural origin with juniper berries.

(b) The minimum alcoholic strength by volume of gin shall be 37.5 %.

(c) Only natural and/or nature-identical flavouring substances as defined in Article 1(2)(b)(i) and (ii) of Directive 88/388/EEC and/or flavouring preparations as defined in Article 1(2)(c) of that Directive shall be used for the production of gin so that the taste is predominantly that of juniper.

Distilled gin

(a) Distilled gin is:

(i) a juniper-flavoured spirit drink produced exclusively by redistilling organoleptically suitable ethyl alcohol of agricultural origin of an appropriate quality with an initial alcoholic strength of at least 96% vol. in stills traditionally used for gin, in the presence of juniper berries and of other natural botanicals provided that the juniper taste is predominant, or

(ii) the mixture of the product of such distillation and ethyl alcohol of agricultural origin with the same composition, purity and alcoholic strength; natural and/or nature-identical flavouring substances and/or flavouring preparations as specified in category (c), above, may also be used to flavour distilled gin.

(b) The minimum alcoholic strength by volume of distilled gin shall be 37.5%.

(c) Gin obtained simply by adding essences or flavourings to ethyl alcohol of agricultural origin is not distilled gin.

London gin

(a) London gin is a type of distilled gin:

(i) obtained exclusively from ethyl alcohol of agricultural origin, with a maximum methanol content of 5 grams per hectolitre of 100% vol. alcohol, whose flavour is introduced exclusively through the re-distillation in traditional stills of ethyl alcohol in the presence of all the natural plant materials used,

(ii) the resultant distillate of which contains at least 70% alcohol by vol.,

(iii) where any further ethyl alcohol of agricultural origin is added it must be consistent with the characteristics listed in Annex I(1), but with a maximum methanol content of 5 grams per hectolitre of 100% vol. alcohol,

(iv) which does not contain added sweetening exceeding 0.1 gram of sugars per litre of the final product nor colorants,

(v) which does not contain any other added ingredients other than water.

(b) The minimum alcoholic strength by volume of London gin shall be 37.5 %.

(c) The term London gin may be supplemented by the term 'dry'.

Pastis

(a) Pastis is an aniseed-flavoured spirit drink that also contains natural extracts of liquorice root, which implies the presence of the colorants known as 'chalcones' as well as glycyrrhizic acid, the minimum and maximum levels of which must be 0.05 and 0.5 grams per litre respectively.

(b) The minimum alcoholic strength by volume of pastis shall be 40%.

(c) Only natural flavouring substances and preparations as defined in Article 1(2)(b)(i) and Article 1(2)(c) of Directive 88/388/EEC may be used in the preparation of pastis.

(d) Pastis contains less than 100 grams of sugars per litre, expressed as invert sugar, and has a minimum and maximum anethole level of 1.5 and 2 grams per litre respectively.

Liqueur

(a) Liqueur is a spirit drink:

(i) having a minimum sugar content, expressed as invert sugar, of:

– 70 grams per litre for cherry liqueurs, the ethyl alcohol of which consists exclusively of cherry spirit,

       – 80 grams per litre for gentian or similar liqueurs prepared with gentian or similar plants as the sole aromatic substance,

       – 100 grams per litre in all other cases;

  (ii) produced by flavouring ethyl alcohol of agricultural origin or a distillate of agricultural origin or one or more spirit drinks or a mixture thereof, sweetened and with the addition of products of agricultural origin or foodstuffs such as cream, milk or other milk products, fruit, wine or aromatised wine as defined in Council Regulation (EEC) No 1601/91 of 10 June 1991 laying down general rules on the definition, description and presentation of aromatized wines, aromatized wine-based drinks and aromatized wine-product cocktails.

(b) The minimum alcoholic strength by volume of liqueur shall be 15%.

Sloe gin

(a) Sloe gin is a liqueur produced by maceration of sloes in gin with the possible addition of sloe juice.

(b) The minimum alcoholic strength by volume of sloe gin shall be 25%.

(c) Only natural flavouring substances and preparations as defined in Article 1(2)(b)(i) and Article 1(2)(c) of Directive 88/388/EEC may be used in the preparation of sloe gin.

(d) The sales denomination may be supplemented by the term 'liqueur'.

Honey or mead nectar

(a) Honey or mead nectar is a spirit drink produced by flavouring the mixture of fermented honey mash and honey distillate and/or ethyl alcohol of agricultural origin, which contains at least 3% vol. of fermented honey mash.

(b) The minimum alcoholic strength by volume of honey or mead nectar shall be 22%.

(c) Only natural flavouring substances and preparations as defined in Article 1(2)(b)(i) and Article 1(2)(c) of Directive 88/388/EEC may be used in the preparation of honey or mead nectar provided that the honey taste is predominant.

(d) Honey or mead nectar may be sweetened only with honey.

Botanicals

Botanicals are the herbs, spices, fruits and other ingredients that give gin its flavour. Many microdistillers have searched beyond the traditional botanicals to find new signature aromas and flavours, sourcing such ingredients as lemongrass, cucumber, bog myrtle, clover and peppermint, often making a virtue of including those that grow close to the place of distillation.

The list of 'new age' botanicals is very long indeed, but most of the leading botanicals have featured in gin recipes for well over a century. Here are the 'top ten' botanicals used in the production of gin, in descending order of popularity:

- **Juniper:** there are more than 50 species of juniper in the world, and juniper berries give gin its defining aromas and flavours of spruce and pine. According to EU law, gin must be predominantly flavoured by Juniprus communis. Without juniper, there is no gin.
- **Coriander:** coriander seeds give spicy, aromatic qualities to gin, and coriander is present in at least 80 per cent of all gins.
- **Angelica:** the third principal botanical used in gin, along with juniper and coriander, angelica is not dissimilar to juniper, but muskier and woodier.
- **Orange:** bitter, Seville-style oranges are those most favoured by gin makers, and the essential oil is contained in the peel, or rind.
- **Lemon:** as with oranges, the essential oils required by distillers are found in the lemon peel, and several leading gin brands, including Gordon's and Beefeater, use lemon as one of their botanicals.
- **Orris root:** dried orris root delivers strong aromas of violets.
- **Liquorice:** the distinctive aroma and flavour of liquorice root was frequently used in Old Tom-style gins in the past, often to disguise the roughness of the spirit itself.
- **Cardamom:** cardamom seeds add a pungent, slightly peppery character to gins, and have become increasingly popular as a gin botanical in recent years.
- **Cassia:** sourced from the bark of a tree native to Southern China, cassia is sometimes confused with cinnamon, to which it is related. The cinnamon-like aromas and flavours of cassia are powerful, and it must be used sparingly in order not to overpower the gin.
- **Cinnamon:** derived from the Cinnamomum verum tree native to Sri Lanka, cinnamon tends to be less common than cassia as a gin botanical, principally because cassia is more easily sourced.

Case study

Winchester Distillery
www.winchhesterdistillery.co.uk

Winchester distillery was established in 2014 by Paul Bowler, who admits that prior to starting out making gin in his home kitchen in the Hampshire city he had little relevant experience. "I'd spent most of my career working in software development with large corporate clients," he explains, "but I spent the first two years after graduating in the early 1990s working for Merrydown Cider in East Sussex. This gave me an introduction into the dynamics of the drinks industry, which never really left me.

"The last 10 years of my career was spent helping large organisations become more innovative using novel management techniques that allowed them to launch software products quickly and successfully. I built the distillery using the same 'lean' principles, so I didn't leave all my experience behind."

When the fledgling business outgrew Bowler's house, he looked around for suitable commercial premises, but, as he explains, "When I needed to expand I found there was very little available locally of the right size at the right price to support a growing startup, but fortunately discovered our current location at Manor Factory in Old Alresford through a chance conversation. The space we're in already had a bottling licence from a previous owner, has spring water on tap (along with an extraction licence) and has watercress growing outside."

At this point, the relevance of watercress should be explained, and Bowler says that "The distillery is based in the heart of Hampshire's watercress beds, and it has been cultivated at the site since the 1850s. We use this fresh from the field to create our 'Twisted Nose' watercress gin. I believe we are the only commercial gin to use watercress as a botanical. The Romans knew watercress as Nasturtium, meaning 'twisted nose,' from which our gin takes its name.

He adds that "Local Juniper is not particularly prevalent or of the high quality we expect for our gins, so we source from where it grows best. We use herbs such as watercress and lavender, and spices such as coriander seed that are cultivated locally, and we are planning on using Hampshire grain for our commercial neutral spirit and whisky once our current expansion is complete. We're also looking into using grassland around the distillery to grow our own herbs."

When it comes to creating gin recipes, Paul Bowler takes what might be termed a 'scientific approach.' "Initially I distill each botanical individually and then blend them together using ideas from classic food recipes or flavour dictionaries (or simply intuition)," he explains. "We currently have over 200 botanical distillates in the distillery laboratory to work with. Once a blend has been decided we can then work back to a recipe that we can then tune and distill in larger batches."

When it comes to neutral grain spirit (NGS), Winchester distillery both purchases it and distils some of its own. Bowler says that "We buy in spirit that, after further distillation, we use in most of our gins but also increasingly make neutral spirit ourselves for various products.

"We don't yet have the capacity to make neutral spirit in the quantities that we'd need for all of our rectified spirits but expect this to change with our current distillery expansion. We are experimenting with wheat and barley for our NGS, as well as other base ingredients such as rye and corn."

When it comes to the treatment of botanicals, Winchester uses both steeping and vapour infusion, with Paul Bowler explaining that "We use the most appropriate method to suit each botanical and the expression of spirit we are making. For example, for some gin recipes we macerate select botanicals for a period of time before distillation, whilst for others the botanicals go straight in the still with the spirit. The use of vapour infusion is suitable for delicate botanicals such as fresh flowers, or for fresh citrus peels where the oils can become stewed if distilled in the pot, and we use this method for speciality gins such as our Hampshire Fine and seasonal limited editions."

The stills used by Winchester range from small Hoga copper alembics (5–30 litres) from Portugal and stainless-steel stills from Germany (30–150 litres), the largest of which includes a six-section column and vapour infusion chambers. According to Paul bowler, "We'll planning on getting in 500 or 1,000 litres stills for our expansion to help increase production of our neutral spirit and to take our rum and whisky into full production."

Winchester benefitted by being the first craft distillery to open in Hampshire, and Bowler reveals that "From a starting point of zero we were profitable in the first six months and have doubled turnover in all of the four years we've been trading. We cannot rest on our laurels though – it is a dynamic and highly competitive industry with new spirits (gins especially) seemingly launching every week.

"Our goal for this year is to increase distribution further across the UK and find international agents and distributors to increase our export sales. We must never forget our roots though, and any growth must not damage our core values and Hampshire focus.

"We're taking on more of the building in order to increase the capacity of our fermentation and distilling operations and produce new spirits – brandy, rum and whisky – in commercial batches. We're moving our desks into new offices within the building, refurbishing one unit into a cask ageing room, and transforming a larger unit into the new distillery with a dedicated bottling room and finished goods storage area.

"This will free up the current distillery area to become our full-time research and development laboratory, and a place where we can run consumer distilling sessions for our gin school. It will also enable our current office to be transformed into a full-time visitor space, complete with a retail shop, for tastings, masterclasses and corporate events.

"These distillery experiences are always popular and create instant cash-flow, vital for a growing business. Once people see what we're doing, experience the care and attention to detail in our spirit production and have tasted the end result, they become unofficial ambassadors and help spread the word."

With the business thriving and expanding, what does Bowler consider the main challenges he has faced to get to this stage? "Initially, the main challenge was getting a product idea to market. There are various HMRC and local government licenses to obtain before you can start. You then have your recipe to formulate, branding to create and raw materials to source. Next, you must safely create the end product in compliance with trading standards, health and safety legislation and HMRC duty schemes.

"You then have to get to learn the workings of the spirits industry, start growing sales accounts, work with wholesalers and distributors, understand employment law, manage cash-flow, register trademarks (and fight infringements), attend exhibitions and trade shows, create marketing and PR, deal with new competitors popping up and a whole host of other problems. You don't start a distillery if you want an easy life, no matter how romantic the idea sounds!"

Consultants

Whatever your level of distilling knowledge, the involvement of an experienced consultant can ensure the creation of a cost-effective, efficient and reliable distilling business. The financial outlay involved in securing their services is usually money well spent.

The Craft Distilling Business
www.thecraftdistillingbusiness.com
The Craft Distilling Business has been established by Matt Servini and Vanesa Rapier to offer a comprehensive service to start-up distillers. Its modus operandi features the use of duty-paid neutral grain spirit, and the company provides site surveys, design and commission of stills, recipe creation, health & safety and HMRC licencing advice, maintenance, staff training, marketing and packaging support. Additionally, the firm sources botanicals and neutral spirit for its customers.

A portable still – named Gertie – is also available to hire for pop-ups and other events. Gertie can produce any unaged spirits to existing or bespoke recipes.

Craft Distillery Design
www.craftdistillerydesign.com
Based at Ballindalloch in the heart of Speyside, Craft Distillery Design offers "A bespoke service in craft distillery design and development for prospective artisan and craft distillers from initial concept through to first production."

The company specialises in small-scale distilling ventures, and works with clients through the formation of business strategies, site appraisal and procurement, architecture and planning, distilling equipment selection and project management, even working where necessary to help create brand identities.

Craft Distillery Design's best-known clients have included Ballindalloch and the Cotswolds distilleries.

Organic Distilleries
www.organicdistilleries.co.uk
Organic Distilleries is headed up by architect Gareth Roberts, and is based at Helensburgh, in the Argyll & Bute area of Scotland. The company describes itself as "…an affiliation of experienced consultants," and services provided include business planning, distillery build design and marketing expertise, see page 7.

Techni-K Consulting
www.techni-k.co.uk
All start-up distillers who plan to sell their spirit commercially must by law have a HACCP (Hazard Analysis and Critical Control Points) plan that meets UK legislation standard. Techni-K Consulting (based in Derbyshire) has produced a specific Distillery HACCP, and as the company explains, "Our Distillery HACCP has been designed to provide all the necessary documentation you need, so all you need to do is amend it to the specific processing of your product following our detailed guidelines using our step-by-step workbook. What you will be relieved to know is that it's 95 per cent completed for you already!"

Langley Distillery
www.langleydistillery.co.uk
Langley distillery in Hertfordshire was established in 1920 to produce gin, and now specialises in creating London Dry Gin for a range of customers. Additionally, Langley supplies neutral grain spirit (NGS) and bespoke botanicals for clients wishing to make their own gins, along with grain, molasses, rye and barley spirit, plus vodka, whisky, brandy and rum – all available in quantities from five litres to 1,000 litres, and full/part tankers.

Training

The use of consulting professionals is one way of ensuring you start out with the optimum distilling potential, but expanded personal knowledge and ongoing education can also be invaluable.

The Institute of Brewing & Distilling
www.ibd.org.uk
The Institute of Brewing & Distilling (IBD) is the world's leading professional body for people working in brewing and distilling. As an international professional and educational body, the IBD promotes "The advancement of the education and professional development in the science and technology of brewing, distilling, and related industries." Dating back to 1886, the IBD now boasts over 5,000 members and is the largest global professional body for brewers and distillers, and the only one with a worldwide footprint.

The IBD offers the following qualifications:

Case study

Allen Associates
www.allenhpe.co.uk

Headed by managing director Professor Scott Allen, the company is based at Stirling in Central Scotland, with a second office at Craigellachie in the Speyside whisky-making region. Allen provides a range of engineering solutions from initial consultation to delivery of turnkey distillery projects.

One of Allen Associates' innovations is the iMash system, which is aimed at small-scale distillers and provides integrated mashing and fermenting facilities in one flexible, easy to install and cost-effective unit.

It can also be used in conjunction with a larger planned new distillery build, reducing the time to market for mature spirit by at least 12 months by allowing the production of spirit whilst the main distillery is being constructed. Allen Associates has now introduced the option to distillers of hiring or leasing the system to suit such projects.

With microdistillers especially in mind, Allen Associates has teamed up with master blender Henric Molin from Spirit of Hven distillery in Sweden. The partnership can assist start-up distillers from recipe creation and conceptual design through to commissioning and maturation.

Recipes can be tested at Hven distillery to ensure that customers are totally happy with the product before committing capital to a new facility, and they may also attend recipe trials – staying at the onsite five star hotel - to observe the process and gain an understanding of the operation. Additionally, they have access to Hven's state-of-the-art laboratory, complete with gas chromatographer and mass spectrometer (GC-MS) to help fine-tune the recipe and flavour characteristics of their spirit.

One of Allen Associates more recent consultancies was for the Raasay distillery situated in the inner Hebrides. A meeting on the beautiful island of Raasay on a wild winter's day in January 2015 was the starting point for a journey that would see the creation of a stunning new Scottish distillery incorporating a mix of distilled spirits technology.

Working with Alasdair Day (co-founder of R&B Distillers), Martin Smith utilised Allen Associates' virtual reality system to bring the designs to life, while cooling jackets on the fermenters and a six-plate column on the spirit still added a novel approach in craft malt distilling.

As with most distillery projects the initial tasks were to prepare a typical distillery footprint and a distillery mass and energy balance to confirm production capacity and service consumptions. This was achieved within a few weeks to assist with the planning application and confirming an overall budget for the project, which was issued for final project funding.

A common challenge in distillery design is pipework layout, and the Raasay project was no different. To deal with the issue Allen Associates worked closely with Garry Fraser at LH Stainless and prepared a virtual reality 3D model of the distillery. The state-of-the-art technology allowed the design team to review the layout in the virtual reality environment so any issues could be solved prior to the site build. This was particularly important when working with a remote site.

The initial distillery capacity decided on was a one tonne mash system capable of producing approximately 90,000 lpa (litres per annum) operating at one mash per day, five days a week. In July 2018 this was increased to two shifts on five days a week, with volumes increasing to 188,000 lpa. It is important to note that although the volumes put Raasay firmly in the craft rather than microdistillery category, the same techniques and high standards exist across both.

The new distillery was designed to relevant standards and guidance to ensure process safety compliance. The recent DSEAR risk assessment had no recommendations proving the plant was designed as per industry best practice.

A coordinated, team-driven approach ensured that 32 months on from that initial meeting Allen Associates and distillery managers Chris Anderson and Iain Robertson were ready to get the first spirit off the stills for the official opening on 16 September 2017.

Fundamentals of Distilling (Novice): the purpose of this qualification is to provide a basic grounding in the technical features of brewing and packaging of beers and distilling of spirits for both production personnel and for people employed in brewery or distillery companies (and related industries), but in non-technical roles.

This course is suitable for all non-technical personnel employed within the distilling industry who would benefit from background knowledge in distilling production, (sales, marketing, HR, finance) or anyone who has just started a technical career within the distilling industry.

General Certificate in Distilling (Intermediate): This qualification is suitable for all non-technical personnel employed in the distilling industry who would benefit from background knowledge in spirit production and for those who have just commenced their technical or production careers.

General Certification in Distilling (GCD) requires a basic knowledge of the processes used to produce the main types of potable spirit consumed worldwide. The scope of the present GCD syllabus is therefore confined to spirits derived either from cereals, cane sugar and cane sugar molasses, and grapes.

Diploma in Distilling: these learning courses are designed to guide candidates through the examination syllabus. Typical Diploma in Distilling candidates are team leaders and operational managers.

There are three Modules to the Diploma in Distilling Examination.
- Module 1: Preparation of Fermentable Extract 1A: Cereal wort 1B: Molasses wort 1C: Grapes must
- Module 2: Fermentation, Distillation & Maturation
- Module 3: Process Technology

Heriot Watt University, Edinburgh
www.hw.ac.uk
For the truly serious distiller with time to commit, Edinburgh's Heriot Watt University Brewing & Distilling qualifications are highly regarded the world over. BSc Hons (Undergraduate level) and MSc/Diploma (Postgraduate level) programmes are available, and the Postgraduate Diploma/MSc programme is accredited by the Institute of Brewing & Distilling.

BrewLab

www.brewlab.co.uk

BrewLab Ltd is based in Sunderland, Tyne & Wear, and as its name suggests, the principal focus is on brewing. However, the organisation has now developed a three-day Start Up Distilling Course which is proving popular with would-be microdistillers. According to BrewLab, "We find it best to learn from professionals within the industry, which is why we bring in working distillers and specialists to take you through the different stages of the distillery process and give practical advice on start-up issues.

"Not only do we offer specially developed facilities but the course also gives you access to staff with extensive experience in brewing and distilling who are accredited in quality teaching schemes with a range of support facilities including online support."

Gin schools

A growing number of gin distilleries run training courses in gin production. For example, Jamie Baxter operates a Gin School at his 45 West distillery **www.45westdistillers.com** in Leicestershire, as do Salcombe Distillery Co in Devon **www.salcombegin.com**, Nelson's Gin Distillery at Uttoxeter, Staffordshire **www.nelsonsgin.co.uk,** and Manchester's Three Rivers **www.manchesterthreerivers.com.**

Equipping your distillery

Whether you decide to go it alone and source your own distilling equipment, with or without input from specialist consultants, or contract a company to create a complete distillery for you, there are a number of essential pieces of kit required to make spirits. The following list applies to those intending to undertake the full spirit-making process themselves.

Many gin distillers buy in grain neutral spirit (GNS) from other distilleries and create their own distinctive brand by the selection of botanicals used. Some even have the entire product made for them by a third party, and simply 'badge' it with their name. Given that provenance is at the heart of what most microdistillers are all about, this latter practice tends to be frowned upon by many in the business. Gin may also be produced by adding flavourings to GNS, with the intention of creating a predominant taste of juniper. This method of production is known as 'compounding.'

If you plan to buy in base spirit to create gin, rather than distil your own from scratch, then only the section relating to stills will apply.

Case study

Fulton Boilers
www.fulton.co.uk

Fulton Ltd specialises in the design and manufacture of steam, hot water, thermal fluid boilers, packaged plant rooms and skid-mounted systems for industrial, commercial and medical applications. One of it's recent installations was at Sipsmith Distillery in London.

Established in Hammersmith in 2009, Sipsmith Distillery is a small independent business that, using the first copper still to launch in London for almost 200 years, crafts truly artisanal gins and vodkas.

The distillery gives female names to each of its stills and the first, Prudence (designed and built by Carl Distilleries near Stuttgart, Germany), originally used electricity to power elements in the steam jacket surrounding it. But, as Sipsmith's export market grew and production increased, the founders realised additional stills were required to meet demand. The company's second still, named Patience, is another 300 litre still that also used electric elements to heat the steam jacket. But it wasn't until a third and larger still – the 1,500 litre Constance – was required that the company decided to switch from an electrically-heated process to one using a steam boiler.

Commenting for Fulton, managing director Carl Knight says: "We visited Sipsmith Distillery when they were using German electrically powered stills but wanted to install a gas-fired steam boiler for their new, larger premises. Our area manager discussed the specifications and options with them and an order was subsequently placed for a Fulton 20J vertical boiler and associated ancillaries. We continued to provide assistance and technical support throughout the installation and during commissioning."

As Carl goes on to explain, many craft breweries and distilleries start off using electric but, as they reach the right size and output, quickly move to steam-based systems such as those from Fulton. "While electric systems can be quite efficient, they only heat the water required for the steam jacket, so are not as manageable or controllable as steam boiler-based systems." says Carl.

Felix James, Head of Operations at Sipsmith Distillery, says: "For us, the difference is the same as cooking using electric or gas.

Prudence and Patience both used electric elements initially but, to control the water temperature, you could only switch on or off the four elements in the steam jacket. And then there would be a delayed response as it would take time to transfer the energy through to the stills. With steam, once it's turned down or off, the stills are very quick to shut down or respond to the temperature change." He goes on to say that unlike 'big plant' distillation processes that can produce a spirit in less than two hours, each Sipsmith gin or vodka distilling process takes up to eight or nine hours to complete.

Steam from the Fulton 20J boiler is gradually introduced into the still's steam jacket until the NGS inside the still reaches 78.3 degrees centigrade, the boiling point of alcohol. As the wash boils and turns to vapour, it rises through the still's helmet and swan's neck before returning to liquid form in the condenser. After the initial 'heads' cut (containing methanol) and the final 'tails' cut are disposed of, the 1,500-litre Constance produces approximately 950 litres at still strength (82 per cent for the gin and 90 per cent for the vodka). This distilled liquid is then cut with water to create a bottling strength product that makes up to 2,500 bottles. The smaller 300 litre stills Prudence and Patience can produce up to 500 bottles each per run, with Patience currently being used to produce predominantly new products or for product development.

Explaining the reasons for specifying Fulton, Felix mentioned the ties with nearby Fuller's Brewery that uses Fulton's boilers in the brewing process. "Fulton are very well respected and, being a UK manufacturer, are very easy to deal with. We undertake our own water analysis every month but do have a service contract with Fulton, which visits the site every three months to conduct its own analysis and check the condition of the boiler and the system. This proved invaluable on one occasion when, between Fulton visits, we had dosed too much chemical into the feed water tank. However, Fulton was on hand, its technician was very helpful and offered the correct procedure for a solution."

An additional benefit for the distillery is that all condensate from the boiler's steam raising process is returned to the feed tank to reduce energy and further improve the system's efficiency.

Making infusions

When making gin, there are two ways to extract aroma and flavour from botanicals. The first is to steep them in the base spirit for a period of up to 48 hours (maceration), though usually significantly less. This method is followed by major brands such as Beefeater. The second is the infusion method – favoured by Bombay Sapphire, among other best-selling gins – for which a botanical basket will be required. The word 'basket' is something of a misnomer, since the equipment in question is really a metal cylinder, with a screw-on lid and a fine mesh in the base to allow the botanicals to infuse into the base spirit as it boils. The basket is suspended in the still above the level of liquid, with which it never comes into direct contact.

Some distillers combine steeping and infusion, subsequently blending the two distillates. A classic example is Hendrick's Gin, where one still is used to steep botanicals for 24 hours before boiling, while the second still uses vapour infusion with different botanicals.

Making liqueurs

If making liqueurs, the only additional piece of kit you are likely to require is a vessel in which to steep the flavouring – fruit, spices and even beans or roots. Ideally, opt for an IBC (Intermediate Bulk Container), usually made from blow-moulded HDPE high-density polyethylene or ideally polythene. Common sizes are 600 litres and 1,000 litres.

Hot liquor tank

The word 'liquor' is rather misleading here, as this tank never contains any alcohol. It is the vessel in which water is heated prior to the mashing process. In brewing parlance, 'liquor' is water. The Hot Liquor Tank – or HLT – is essentially, an insulated stainless steel tank fitted with a heating element, usually powered by electricity.

Mash tun

The mash tun is the vessel in which ground malted barley or grist is mixed with hot water to convert its starch content into fermentable sugars. Early mash tuns were made of wood, but these had limited lifespans and cast iron became the norm, now usually replaced by stainless steel. Some mash tuns are open-topped, but most modern ones are covered in order to limit loss of heat. Older distillery mash tuns tended to be equipped with a system of rakes to stir the grist/ hot water mix and maximise extraction, but modern 'lauter' mash tuns are fitted with large, circling arms with blades attached, and floors that sieve the solids from the liquid. Lauter tuns are efficient in terms of yield and also speed of operation. The liquid produced during mashing is known as worts.

Fermenting vessels

Often known as 'washbacks', these vessels are where alcohol is produced for the first time during the distilling process. The wort created in the mash tun is pumped into the washbacks, where yeast is added in order to facilitate fermentation. Washbacks were traditionally made from wood – usually Oregon pine or larch – but many distilleries now feature stainless steel washbacks, which are easier to clean than their wooden counterparts. Most washbacks are fitted with 'switchers,' or mechanical blades that spin around and prevent an overflow of liquid as the yeast acts on the wort during fermentation. After fermentation has ceased, the alcoholic liquid produced is termed wash.

Boiler

If you plan to make rum, then a boiler will be required in addition to fermentation vessels and stills. Prior to fermentation, molasses must be reduced with water, and due to its viscous consistency, the reduction necessitates boiling. A boiler – also known as a copper – intended for use in brewing is ideal for this purpose.

Stills

Whatever style and make of still or stills you choose, the purpose is the same – to separate alcohol from water in the wash by means of heating. This is achievable because alcohol boils at a lower temperature than water.

Pot stills

Pot stills are traditionally associated with the production of Scotch single malt and Irish pure (or single) pot still whiskey. They operate on a batch distillation basis as opposed to continual distillation, which is practiced in column stills. They are made from copper, which is malleable and easy to shape as well as an excellent conductor of heat. Copper also facilitates important flavour changes during distillation. In Scotland, pot stills are usually used in pairs to distil malt whisky, while the Irish practice is to triple distil pot still whiskey in three individual stills. Some microdistillers, however, operate just a single pot still and use it for two consecutive distillations.

The size and design of a pot still can impact significantly on the type of spirit it produces, with greater copper content serving to produce a lighter style, though the permutations of pot still distillation mean that still size and design are just two variables to take into account. The amount of wash contained in a still, the speed at which it is distilled and variable operating temperatures all affect the 'new-make' that ultimately flows from the spirit still, as do the 'cut points' at which the 'heart of the run' are separated from the less pure foreshots and feints.

Traditionally, copper pot stills were heated by direct firing, using coal, coke or even peat, but since the late 19th century, the use of steam to heat stills has been practiced, and direct firing is now rare. Where it is employed, such as Glenfarclas whisky distillery on Speyside, the source of heat is usually gas. Steam is introduced to the stills through coils or 'pans' fitted in the base, and the major advantage of this method of heating wash is that it is much more controllable than direct firing, leading to greater consistency in the final spirit.

Column stills

The continuous still, comprising two interconnected 'columns' was developed by Scottish distiller Robert Stein, who patented his invention in 1827. It allowed unmalted grain to be distilled into alcohol on a far larger scale than was possible in traditional copper pot stills, and that alcohol was also considerably cheaper to make, thanks to the requirement for only a small amount of relatively malted barley to be included in the mash bill. The character of the sprit produced was also notably consistent.

Stein's still design was improved upon in terms of simplicity and efficiency by Irishman Aeneas Coffey, who patented the Coffey Still in 1830. Coffey's apparatus comprised two large parallel columns, the analyser and the rectifier, parallel to the wash still and spirit still in a pot still distillery, with internal plates of perforated copper. The design of most column stills remains relatively unchanged to this day, and steam is the usual source of heat.

Hybrid stills

Hybrid stills are a combination of pot and column still, interlinked with piping, instrumentation and 'diverter' valves, designed to prevent cross-contamination if distilling different products. They are popular with gin distillers who re-distil neutral spirit in the pot element along with the botanicals, which are steeped before boiling, or in the case of vapour infusion, placed in a 'basket' above the spirit and the vapour created during boiling is infused with the botanicals. Whichever method is used, the resultant spirit is then distilled again through the column still to remove remaining undesirable compounds.

Vacuum distillation

Whisky distiller William Grant & Sons Ltd uses vacuum distillation at its large scale Girvan grain distillery in Ayrshire, but a number of smaller gin producers – such as Cambridge, Sacred Spirits and Victory Gin Distillery – have also adopted this method, believing it leads to fresher flavours in the ultimate product.

From a technical standpoint, producing spirit under vacuum reduces the atmospheric pressure, allowing distillation to take place at significantly lower temperatures than in a pot still and by doing so, also saves energy costs. This ensures that more delicate botanicals are not 'cooked,' leading to a marked reduction in their influence on flavour. When distilling under vacuum, the botanicals are initially macerated in neutral alcohol to maximise extraction of flavours.

Manufacturers

Today's start-up distiller is fortunate in that as microdistilling has grown in popularity, so the range of companies providing equipment has also increased. Many of the following firms offer 'turnkey' distilling services, where they act as a single point of contact for the customer and create entire distilleries from scratch ready to be fired up, but will also produce bespoke items of kit to personal specifications. They also usually offer a great degree of flexibility in terms of scale.

John Dore & Co Ltd
www.johndore.co.uk
The oldest distillery engineering business in the world, John Dore is the successor company to Aeneas Coffey & Sons, founded in Dublin in 1830, with a London operation being established five years later. In 1872, John Dore, the works foreman, took over the business from the son of Aeneas Coffey, himself famous as the man behind the patent, column or Coffey still. Dore ran the business from Bromley-by-Bow in London, but in the late 1960 a local authority housing development forced the firm to move to Essex, and today it is based

at Guildford in Surrey. Since 1992 the company has been owned by David Pym, who acquired it from the last member of the Dore family to have an involvement.

John Dore & Co Ltd offers design and consultancy services, and manufactures pot stills for gin and rum (from 500 litres capacity upwards), and whisky (1,000 litres upwards) and also column stills of varying sizes, not to mention a wide variety of tanks and heat exchangers. The firm also specifies and sources all other equipment necessary to create a working distillery.

Briggs plc
www.briggsplc.co.uk
With a pedigree dating back some 270 years in the brewing and distilling industry, Briggs is one of the most respected names in process engineering and also offers consultancy and design services. Additionally, the firm has interests in food, pharmaceuticals, health and beauty products and biofuels, with bases in the former brewing 'capital' of Burton-on-Trent in the UK and Rochester, New York State, in the USA. Briggs produces equipment for mashing, fermenting and distilling, and has taken a leading role in energy and water reduction techniques.

Forsyths
www.forsyths.com
Forsyths is based in the Moray village of Rothes in Scotland's Speyside whisky-making region, and when it comes to distillery fabrication the firm is practically royalty. Established in 1890, Forsyths is now in the hands of the third and fourth generations of the Forsyth family, and has grown to become a global player in the world of distilling while also having significant interests in the oil and gas industries. Forsyths has been responsible for creating large-scale facilities such as the new Macallan distillery, just a few miles from its headquarters, and equipped with no fewer than 36 pot stills, giving a potential annual capacity of some 15mla. On a much smaller scale, Forsyths provided a turnkey service for the 0.5-tonne batch size Cotswolds distillery in Warwickshire and for the one tonne batch size Ballindalloch distillery on Speyside.

McMillan
www.mcmillanltd.co.uk
Another classic Scottish company with coppersmithing at its

heart is McMillan Ltd, based at Prestonpans near Edinburgh. The firm was founded in 1867 and originally operated as Archibald McMillan Ltd. The company boasts that "There can scarcely be a whisky distillery in Scotland, a gin distillery in England or a rum distillery in the Caribbean that has not employed distillation plant manufactured by ourselves." McMillan designs and fabricates everything from botanical chambers for gin distillation, fermenting vessels, pot and column stills, spirit safes, and all the pipework necessary to create an integrated distilling venture.

LH Stainless
www.l-h-s.co.uk
Speyside Copper Works
www.speysidecopper.com
LH Stainless is based in the premises of the former Towiemore distillery near Dufftown on Speyside, and offers a wide range of design, fabrication and installation services for distilleries of all scales. The firm will build gin stills from 200 litres capacity upwards, constructing them either from stainless steel, copper or a mixture of the two. All copperwork is undertaken by associate company Speyside Copper Works, located a few miles away in the Moray capital of Elgin.

Carl
www.brewing-distilling.com
Carl is Germany's oldest distillery fabricator, established in 1869 and based near Stuttgart. The company is an attractive option for small-scale distillers, producing kit from a 50 litre pilot pot still up to a 12,000-litre copper still, along with column stills and everything from single pieces of equipment to full turnkey operations. During recent years there has been a tendency for start-up microdistillers to look to Europe to source their kit, as waiting lists in the UK have sometimes been lengthy, and Arbikie and Sipsmith distilleries are just two in the UK to be equipped with Carl stills.

Frilli
www.frillisrl.com
Like Carl, Frilli is an old-established European distillery fabricator, with the family firm having been formed in Italy back in 1912. Frilli is based in the heart of the Chianti region, 20km from Siena, and offers a wide range of services from feasibility studies to design,

Case Study

Pickering's Gin Distillery
www.pickeringsgin.com

We are all familiar with microdistilleries being set up in weird and wonderful premises, but to the best of our knowledge the Pickering's Gin Distillery in Edinburgh is the only one to be established in former animal kennels.

Pickering's distil, bottle, label and wax their gins by hand at Summerhall, an independent arts community established in what was the Royal (Dick) School of Veterinary Studies. The School has since moved out to modern premises in Roslyn, and that's when the owners of Pickering's Gin come in. Marcus Pickering and Matthew Gammell have been business partners for 12 years and friends for even longer.

Back in 2011 the pair first stepped foot in the old Royal (Dick) Vet School. Hard hats on, Marcus and Matt were ready to renovate. Their building and construction company had been commissioned by the vet school's new proprietor to transform the remarkable old labyrinth of lecture theatres, dissection rooms, stables and laboratories into studios, event spaces, offices and of course a pub!

Marcus took the lead on lettings and filled the complex with artists. An eclectic mix started the community at Summerhall – a brewer, beekeeper, artisanal ice maker, a taxidermist, photographers, illustrators, yogis, printers... the list really does go on. Just when Marcus and Matt thought they were close to completion, their attention was drawn to the old dilapidated animal kennels. "Buckled, so they were," says Marcus. "We needed to find the space a purpose, though." So the pair put the space to the back of their mind and continued with their work, Marcus in the role of Managing Director of Summerhall and Matt responsible for maintenance.

Then, in late 2013, the Pickering's Gin raison d'être – what Matt refers to as their "blueprint" appeared. After 60 years of gathering dust in a London drawer, a curious scrap of brown paper found its way to Marcus following the death of his father. The scrap detailed a recipe, a gin recipe. A genuine artefact that was almost lost to history, the recipe was sent to Marcus by a friend of his late father. The recipe was scribbled down by some spirited distiller in India on July 17 1947. Needless to say, the pair promptly acquired a mini stove-top still and set about distilling this authentic Bombay gin.

It took the pair one year to master the botanical blend, and most importantly, update it. The authentic Bombay gin recipe read like a curry description in an Indian restaurant. The pair are happy to admit that the resulting gin is mind-bogglingly brilliant, "warm, spicy, sweet and jam-packed full of flavour" says Marcus, "not quite what we were expecting, mind you". Marcus and Matt knew what they loved about gin and that is a big hit of juniper and citrus followed by a crisp, dry finish. So, they botanically engineered the original recipe to make it so.

Removing the sweetest ingredient in the recipe – cinnamon – in place of a drying botanical – Angelica root – twisted the character of the distillate. Upping the dried lemon and lime peels and, of course, the juniper, brought about a spectacular gin. Refreshing citrus top notes give way to lingering juniper, finishing with a satisfying spicy bite – a heritage from the original recipe. Using nine botanicals Pickering's Gin is classic but with a huge depth of flavour.

Over the Christmas holidays in 2013 Marcus and Matt set about building themselves a distillery in the dilapidated animal kennels of the old vet school. Intended purely as a hobby, Marcus and Matt financed the project themselves; They installed their first Portuguese alembic still, and, building everything else themselves, the duo sourced non-exploding distillery lights from an old distillery and bought stainless steel Italian wine vats to hold spirit at a fraction of the price of bespoke vessels. They also developed their own method of heating the stills – a bain marie.

There are several ways of heating a pot still - using steam through an internal coil, direct flame or an electric plate under the base. However, some botanicals float and some sink, so with a conventional internal coil some get overheated and some just don't get enough heat. They suspend their stills in bain-marie 'tanks'. "We can control the temperature to within one degree, says Marcus. "All the botanicals go straight into our 500-litre stills and then we steep them."

Pickering's buy in wheat-based neutral grain spirit (NGS), distilled in France, and used by Hendricks among other producers. "It's totally flavourless, as it should be," says Marcus. "You can taste the grain in poorer quality NGS. It makes sense for us to buy this in rather than distil it ourselves. We don't have a farm, we don't have the space and we just want it to be pure."

Pickering's has been a runaway success. Despite small

beginnings the company has more than doubled its output each year. By March 2018, growth was at 33 per cent on the previous year. They now export to over 13 countries, including China, the United States, Australia, New Zealand, Hong Kong and several European countries.

The distillery itself attracts between 300 and 400 visitors each week. Recently awarded Visit Scotland's top award of "Best Visitor Attraction in Edinburgh, the Lothians and Borders" gin enthusiasts can see distillation, bottling and packaging in action.

And what of the opinion that the current "gin-craze" will soon be eclipsed by another drink? "Gin is back to stay, I think," declares Marcus. "It's embedded into the way people drink alcohol now. Drink less - drink better. There are more cocktails based in gin than any other spirit because it's so versatile. I really don't see rum or tequila or whatever coming along and taking over."

construction and project management. The company also offers technical supervision and staff training. Originally specialising in grappa distillation equipment, Frilli now supplies stills for a wide variety of purposes, and in Scotland equipped recent start-ups such as Inchdairnie distillery in Fife, Raasay in the Inner Hebrides and Harris in the Outer Hebrides with whisky and gin making plant.

Holstein

www.a-holstein.de

The firm of Arnold Holstein is based at Markdorf in Germany's Lake Constance region, famous for the cultivation of fruit crops, and Holstein started out producing kit for fruit distillation. Today, the company supplies distilling equipment from a capacity of five litres up to 150 litres for microdistillers, and for larger operations plant with filling capacities from 150 to 6,000 litres. Holstein specialises in distillation systems that combine a copper pot and a rectifying column. Holstein stills are in use at Cotswolds distillery in Warwickshire and Warner Edwards in Northamptonshire, while the firm's first Scotch whisky venture was Lone Wolf.

Hoga

www.hogastills.com

Hoga is based in Galicia, Spain, and has developed a general still fabrication business in recent years while retaining its close connections to the world of wineries. The company produces somewhat exotic-looking 'alembic' style copper stills, which have been installed at many UK microdistilleries, including Bimber in London, Strathearn and Eden Mill in Scotland.

iStill

www.istill.eu

One of the most recent innovations in distillation technology is the iStill, manufactured in the Netherlands. The company makes bold claims for its stainless steel-based stills, declaring that iStill is "… the only automated and robotised distillery line-up in the world. It helps the craft distiller harvest the right tastes, with automated cuts management. Our innovations help create better product more consistently and at lower costs, and with the smallest heads and tails losses in the industry."

iStill capacities vary from 100 litres to 5,000 litres, and according to the manufacturers, "The iStill can mash, ferment and distil any product. One machine does it all, minimising pumping and cleaning and production bottle-neck issues. You can now make whisky, brandy, rum, gin, and vodka on one and the same machine.

"The 21st century technology, together with the compact design and insulation, cut running costs – when compared to traditional plated copper stills – by around 90 per cent, gaining you an amazing competitive advantage over those that wish to continue to use antiquated 19th century technology."

In the UK, iStills are used by Twin River, Blackford, Loch Ness, Verdant Spirits and Dornoch in Scotland, along with the Wrecking Coast distillery at Tintagel in Cornwall.

Raw materials

Alcohol can be made from any substance that contains sugar, but the following are the principal ingredients for UK distilled spirits.

Barley

The sole cereal permitted in the production of single malt whisky is malted barley. A small number of British distilleries make their own malt on site, but most choose to buy in malt from a commercial maltster, specifying any peating levels required and perhaps also specifying barley varieties. Malting barley on a domestic scale is labour intensive and consistency may be hard to achieve, but some distillers, such as Kilchoman on the isle of Islay, consider it worth the effort in order to be able to claim that theirs is a true 'grain to bottle' process.

A number of microdistillers, and particularly those with a related brewing enterprise, choose to use quantities of malt styles usually associated with beermaking, for example pale ale malt, lager malt, crystal malt, brown malt and chocolate malt. Unmalted barley is used in the production of Irish single pot still whiskey and may also be used to make neutral grain spirit (NGS).

Maize

Once the principal grain used to distil grain whisky and neutral grain spirit in the UK, maize has become more expensive than wheat in recent years, and accordingly is used by fewer distillers. The cereal – also known as corn – has its origins in what is now Mexico. Some distillers consider that maize produces a cleaner, sweeter flavours than wheat and is more easily fermentable, also leaving less residue.

Speyside Cooperage LTD

With Speyside Cooperage located in the heart of Malt whisky country and Broxburn Cooperage in the central belt of Scotland, we are ideally situated to service the Scotch whisky industry.

We provide a repair, rebuild and cask rejuvenation service, source and supply casks such as bourbon barrels and sherry, port and Madeira or build new casks to customer specification.

We now part of the Francois Frères' / Demptos group, a French owned cooperage and wood supplier with worldwide interests. This gives Speyside cooperage unrivalled access to casks and oaks from the wine industry.

Francois Frères' has a large research and development facility which works with the drinks industry to provide the perfect product.

THE HOME OF BEAUTIFUL BRITISH
MADE GLASS BOTTLES

ALLIED
Trusted by the World's Finest Brands

ALLIED GLASS, SOUTH ACCOMODATION ROAD, LEEDS LS10 1NQ, TEL +44 (0)113 245 1568
www.allied-glass.com 🐦 @alliedglassUK

Wheat

Now the most commonly used grain to distil grain whisky and NGS, wheat accounts for almost 50 per cent of all cereal grown in the EU. World trade in wheat is greater than all other cultivated crops combined. It was probably first grown in the 'Fertile Crescent' around the Nile, Tigris and Euphrates rivers from c.9,600 BC.

Potatoes

Potatoes were first introduced to Europe in the mid 16th century from their native Peru, and have long been associated with the production of vodka and of illicitly-distilled poitin in Ireland. Many large-scale commercial vodka brands are now made using cereals rather than potatoes, but a number of UK microdistillers such as Chase and Arbikie distil vodka from potatoes, and also use this as the basis for their portfolios of gins.

Molasses

The production of rum begins with sugar cane, usually in the form of molasses, which is a by-product of the sugar-making process. It may also be made from sugar cane juice, but in the UK imported molasses forms the base of rum distillation. The traditional home of rum is the Caribbean and Latin America, where sugar cane is cultivated.

Yeast

A sugar-yielding substance may be key to all distillation, but two other ingredients are also essential. One is yeast, without which fermentation cannot take place. Yeast is a single-celled fungus, and for many years most Scotch whisky distillers have used the M or MX strain of Saccharomyces cerevisiae, though traditionally they favoured a mix of 'distiller's yeast' – to give a high alcohol yield – and 'brewer's yeast' to add mouthfeel and flavour. Distillers such as Adnams and Lone Wolf which take wash from their associated brewing operations to make whisky, use brewer's yeast. Formats of modern distilling yeast include cream, pressed and dried variants. A number of microdistillers are experimenting with different yeast strains, and this element of distilling may well be explored further as operators seek to discover new ways of altering spirit character, however subtly.

Water

Along with yeast, water is the second essential ingredient for any distilling enterprise, as the production of spirit requires significant quantities of H_2O. The water source chosen should be consistent in its supply and pure in character. 'Process water' is used for mashing and cooling purposes and must be free of contaminants, but the water used to reduce the strength of spirit once distilled must meet international standards of potability. Water may be sourced from rivers, lakes/lochs, wells, boreholes or the pubic supply. In England, the Environment Agency allows the free abstraction of 20,000 litres of water per day from wells and boreholes, though a Water Abstraction Licence will be required. If using the public supply, the industrial tariff of water companies will be imposed.

Disposal/water treatment

The waste left over after the brewing and distilling stages of spirit production must be dealt with in a responsible manner, and there is no shortage of legislation intended to ensure that distillers do so. If making gin or vodka, the Wine and Spirits Association (WSA) estimates that it takes 2.5 litres of water to produce one litre of product, though other sources suggest the figure for water usage is higher. Distilleries of all sizes have been concentrating on the issue of reducing waste water, and some of the largest whisky distilleries in Scotland – owned by companies such as Diageo and Pernod Ricard – have made major advances in this area, sometimes by using hot water produced during the distillation stage to heat stills later.

Where neutral alcohol is sourced externally for the production of white spirits, there is less water usage than where full distillation is taking place, but the resultant waste water will have an undesirably low Ph level and contain traces of botanicals. The Environment Agency in England **www.gov.uk/government/organiations/ environment-agency**, Natural Resources Wales **www.gov.wales/ topics/environmentcountrsyside** or the Scottish Environmental Protection Agency (SEPA) in Scotland **www.sepa.org.uk** issue permits for the discharge of waste water into watercourses, and Trade Effluent Consent is required by water supply companies if the intention is to discharge waste water into the sewerage system.

Given sufficient space, a system of reed beds may be established to filter out pollutants from waste water, and such a scheme will enhance your 'green' distilling credentials, as the reed beds will also be highly attractive to wildlife.

When conducting full mash distillations using grains, the

protein-rich spent grains or draff that remains after mashing has traditionally been sold to local farmers as cattle feed, or processed into cattle feed pellets, though it is increasingly being used to power anaerobic digester plants where bio-gas is created, which in turn can be converted into steam energy.

The pot ale and spent lees that remain after distillation are treated to remove unacceptably high levels of copper if necessary, and most of this goes for cattle feed with the remainder being discharged into bodies of water sufficiently large and fast-flowing to accept them without issues of pollution.

Chapter Three
Spirits production

aving explored the heritage of spirits, product definitions and distilling equipment, it's now time to get down to the business of actually making alcohol!

Developing recipes

Single malt whisky

It can be argued that the most straightforward spirit to make in terms of its 'recipe' is single malt whisky. 100 per cent malted barley is the only cereal permitted and the other ingredients are yeast and water.

However, many distillers consider it the most difficult to make and it is often neglected by start-up ventures. While most large-scale distillers are busy making malt whisky from the same mainstream, recently – developed barley varieties, and the most efficient distillers' yeast, microdistillers have the luxury of being able to experiment with barley, malting styles and yeast strains.

Many of what are termed 'heritage' varieties of barley have been abandoned by most distillers because newer types have been developed that are higher yielding and more disease resistant. For the microdistiller, however, yield is not the ultimate objective and the use of virtually redundant barley varieties can give quite significant variations of spirit character.

When it was developed during the 1960s, Golden Promise became a game-changer for the Scotch whisky industry, as it could withstand Scottish winds due to its shorter, stiffer straw, and Scotland was subsequently able to grow most of the barley required for whisky making. Now long abandoned by the mainstream, Golden Promise continued to be used by The Macallan distillery on Speyside for many years due to its ability to create the rich, oily spirit style required, and more recently the Minstrel variety has replaced Golden Promise – as it is able to provide the same characteristics.

A number of microdistillers work with heritage barley varieties, including Toad in Oxford – which has taken grain sourcing to a whole new level and the London Distillery Company.

When it comes to malting the barley, regardless of variety some brewing enterprises with accompanying distilling operations have chosen to experiment with types of malt most usually associated with beer making, including pale malt, chocolate malt, crystal malt and lager malt. Each of these gives a slightly different flavour profile to the spirit being distilled.

It terms of yeast, some microdistillers have eschewed the use of modern distillers' yeast and have reverted to the old practice of mixing brewers' and distillers' yeast. The London Distillery Company, for one, has undertaken research into varying strains of traditional distillers' yeast, and this seems likely to be an area for much greater exploration in future, even though the nuances in character imparted to the spirit itself may be small.

Not all whisky is single malt, of course, and Adnams of Suffolk have produced a 'Triple Malt' whisky made from malted barley, plus wheat and oats, and rye is becoming an increasingly popular grain for microdistillers exploring the whisky genre.

Blended whisky

At present, most UK whisky microdistillers are focusing on single malts or variants such as the Triple Malt noted above. However, as the increasing amount of maturing microdistilled whisky hits the market, and new entrants to the arena opt for whisky making as at least part of their product range, it seems highly likely that limited editions of premium blended whiskies will be developed to expand the sector.

When deciding on the recipe for your blended whisky there are several factors to bear in mind. As a rule of thumb, the higher the percentage of malt whisky compared to grain whisky in the recipe, the better quality the product, and higher prices can therefore be commanded. However, grain whisky is significantly cheaper to buy than malt whisky.

Age of component whiskies is also crucial. Most grain whisky is used for blending when it is four to five years of age, though it can be deployed when significantly aged. Similarly, older malt whiskies give an impression of luxury, but a key factor to bear in mind is that the older the whisky the more expensive it is in the first place.

Stylistically, there are also decisions to make. Are you aiming for a full-bodied, peaty blend, in which case Islay malts will doubtless come into consideration, or is your intention to produce something rich, sherried and postprandial in character? If the latter is your aim, then sherry cask-matured Speyside and Highland malts will play a significant art in your recipe.

Strength is yet another factor to take into account. The 'standard' 40% ABV has now come to feel less than special for upscale whiskies, so bottling at a higher ABV or even at cask strength is an attractive option. Once again, however, it will make your product more expensive to create, though hopefully the achievable price points should make it worthwhile.

It may seem that with some trial and error anyone should be able to assemble a decent blended whisky, but the art of whisky blending is highly skilled, requiring the ability to assemble component spirits that will harmonise and create something greater than the sum of its parts. The art has been likened to a conductor leading an orchestra.

Gin

With regard to gin production, the ingredients become more varied although the recipes are simpler. If you choose to buy in neutral grain spirit (NGS) rather than distil your own, the first variable has already been decided for you, as the NGS in question will have been distilled from either wheat or maize. If, however, you distil from scratch, the choice of raw material is yours to make.

Wheat and barley are the most common grains used, but Adnams' Rising Sun Gin is made from locally grown rye, and the same company's First Rate Triple Malt Gin comprises wheat, barley and oats. Rather than cereal, some producers such as Arbikie and Chase use potatoes as the base for their gin, with the former favouring home-grown King Edward, Cultra and Maris Piper varieties, while the latter cultivates King Edward and Lady Claire.

Whether bought in or distilled on the premises, the NGS is turned into gin by the addition of botanicals, and while juniper is compulsory, and others such as coriander and angelica are almost ubiquitous, many gin distillers source 'signature' botanicals that are ideally unique to them. For example, Isle of Harris Gin **www.harrisdistillery.com** has as its signature botanical sugar kelp, hand-harvested by a local diver, and intended to embody the maritime environment in which the Outer Hebridean distillery operates. Creating the optimum gin recipe can be a lengthy process involving lots of trial and error, combining various permutations and quantities of botanicals until the desired effect is achieved.

Vodka

As with gin, if buying in NGS the choice of grain has already been made, but distilling from scratch gives the opportunity to opt for barley, wheat, rye (Toad's Oxford Rye Vodka) a mixture of wheat, barley and oats (Adnam's Longshore Triple Malt Vodka) or potatoes (Arbikie Potato Vodka).

Liqueurs

A liqueur comprises a distilled spirit that has been flavoured with fruit, cream, herbs, spices, flowers or nuts, and is typically bottled with added sugars. The spirits used are gin, vodka, brandy and whisky.

Nut-based liqueurs are very popular – think coffee, chocolate and big brands like the hazelnut based Frangelico. Herbal liqueurs are also in demand, with Chartreuse (made using no fewer than 130 herbs, plants and flowers) being one of the most recognisable names on the market. Usually, herbal liqueurs are produced from a relatively wide range of botanicals. This category also includes aniseed-based liqueurs such as absinthe and sambuca, and bitter liqueurs like Campari.

Cream liqueurs usually comprise a spirit base, an emulsion of cream and various flavourings. The original cream liqueur was Bailey's, made using Irish whiskey and launched in 1974. Despite widespread emulation and fierce competition, Baileys retains some 25 per cent of the global liqueur market.

A final category of liqueurs comprises those made without neutral alcohol as a base but rather with a flavourful spirit such as Cognac (Grand Marnier) or whisk(e)y (Southern Comfort, Drambuie and the aforementioned Bailey's).

Some liqueurs – such as those based on cream based – are more difficult to perfect and produce than others, therefore it probably makes sense to start with staples already being produced on a craft scale before branching out into more adventurous and innovative directions. For example, Friary Liqueurs of Frome in Somerset **www.friaryliqueurs.co.uk** produces gin-based raspberry, ginger and sloe liqueurs, plus vodka-based chocolate, raspberry, strawberry, toffee and 'Cloudy Lemon' liqueurs.

Casks

It may seem surprising to see 'casks' as an element of spirit recipes, but if you plan to barrel-age gin, vodka or rum, and if whisky is part of your product range, then that is exactly how casks should be viewed. It is estimated that up to 85 per cent of the character of whisky develops during maturation, and the botanicals within gin can be transformed in terms of the flavours they evoke when interaction with wood becomes part of the equation.

Broadly speaking, maturation takes place due to a three way 'conversation' between the spirit, the cask and the external atmosphere. In a small cask the content has much greater contact with the wood than in a large one, and the smaller the cask the faster maturation is likely to occur. Many microdistillers choose to fill casks that are significantly smaller than the traditional whisky industry minimum of a 200 litre barrel, opting for 50 litre octaves.

The two principal types of oak used for spirits maturation are American White Oak (Quercus alba) and European or 'Spanish' oak (Quercus petraea). Of these, American White Oak grows faster, is tighter grained and has fewer knots than its European relative.

Use of a cask that has previously held Bourbon or sherry and is being used for whisky maturation for the first time – known as a first-fill cask – will have a greater influence than a cask being used for the second, third or even fourth time.

Microdistillers tend not to content themselves with ex-Bourbon and ex-sherry casks, however, and more wine casks are being pressed into service, while some are even thinking the unthinkable and working with non-oak woods such as chestnut, though in order to qualify as 'Scotch whisky,' the spirit must be aged in oak casks.

When it comes to white spirits, Adnams is one distiller that has chosen to age vodka – taking its Longshore Vodka and committing it to European oak casks for an unspecified period of time to create a product marketed as North Cove Vodka. Meanwhile, the East London Liquor Company has embarked on an innovative programme of cask finishing for its London Dry Gin, with the first batch spending 14 weeks in new French oak barrels. North of the border, the Glasgow Distillery **www.glasgowdistillery.com** is going down a similar route, ageing some of its Makar Gin for ten weeks in new European oak. Edinburgh's Pickering's Gin has opted to fill quantities of its gin into whisky casks – one representing each of the five single malt producing regions of Scotland, so the consumer can experience gin with a hint of Islay, for instance.

With any cask-ageing programme, it is important to closely monitor the progress of the product. Particularly with white spirits, the balance can tip from the wood imparting positive additional characteristics to overwhelming and dominating very quickly.

Case Study

Spirit Of Yorkshire
www.spiritofyorkshire.com

The county of Yorkshire has long been renowned for its fine ales, and in common with the rest of Britain, Yorkshire has seen an extraordinary level of growth in beer-making enterprises during the past few years. One of these is central of the creation of the county's first single malt whisky distillery.

Wold Top Brewery was established in 2003 by arable farmers Tom and Gill Mellor high on the Yorkshire Wolds, close to the North Sea, but not content with this degree of diversification, Tom Mellor dreamed of making Yorkshire whisky.

Mellor declares that "We started from the position that we had 15 years' experience of making alcohol from barley, creating an initial eight percent wash, and we were good at it. I believe that barley selection, the way it is malted, then mashed and fermented is crucial to both brewing and distilling. Our 15 years of experience in converting the starch into fermentable and usable sugars has been invaluable. Attention to detail in equipment installation, hygiene and quality control are paramount in maintaining consistency.

"Putting robust operating procedures in place and recording everything means that if something feels out of place we stand a chance of understanding why. Working with HMRC for a long time also gives us a respect for the work they are obliged to do and although distilling regulations are different to brewing, the requirements are the same. Initially, the requirements for a whisky distilling licence are much more stringent than for brewing, but in all cases accurate record keeping is a must and a given."

The Mellors decided not to build their distillery on the farm, but to set it up in a small industrial estate in the local village of Hunmanby, alongside a busy road and ideal for attracting visitors.

"Monday and Friday are 'wash days' in the brewery," says Mellor. "The rest of the time we make beer. Having produced the wash, we tanker it and quantities of water from the farm down to the distillery and every mash is made up of 5,000 litres of wash. This gives us a yield of 600 litres per distillation, so we fill around a dozen casks per week."

In addition to a pair of copper stills made by Forsyth of Rothes in Scotland, the distillery is also equipped with a four-plate column still. As Tom Mellor's business partner David Thompson explains, "The column still gives huge reflux if we purify the make coming off the spirit still though it. It gets up to 92% ABV but keeps its fruitiness. It gives us a point of difference to other distilleries, and at present we are working 50:50 on this and spirit made entirely in the pot stills."

The whole operation was developed very much 'under the radar' until the distillery opened to the public at Easter 2017, boasting a coffee shop with viewing windows onto the stills, a retail area and distillery tours.

Tom Mellor says that "Visitor centre numbers are growing weekly and are ahead of expectations. As each holiday period comes upon us (this coastal area is very dependent on tourism) we get more and more people through both the shop and coffee shop. We hold a regular music night every Tuesday and this is developing not just a loyal following, but approximately 60 per cent of people are new each week. We also hold Friday night sessions once a month, and these are not just music but also literary evenings. During the day locals are starting to become regulars, as it becomes the default place to meet."

When it comes to offering advice to would-be distillers, Mellor is blunt. "Do it properly and don't bodge! Seek out and be prepared to pay for the best advice you can. We used the renowned consultant Dr Jim Swan from the very start in 2012 until his untimely death in February 2016.Make sure you set it up and run it as a business, not as a hobby. Whisky making from scratch requires time, patience, money, nerve and a few sleepless nights! Don't skimp on brand strategy and make sure you are clear about where your product fits in the marketplace from the first."

To date, Spirit of Yorkshire has bottled two young expressions under the Maturing Malt label, ahead of a full-scale release in 2019. 2,000 bottles of MM001 and MM002 each sold out within a matter of weeks, and Tom Mellor says that "We are very pleased with the flavour profiles of both releases although each is very different. Jim Swan always commented on the high level of fruit esters in the wash, and together with his recommendations for cask selection (and of course our excellent Yorkshire Coast climate) we feel that there is much to be enthusiastic about in the future."

Making spirits

The business of creating spirits begins with raw fermentable material, whether it be cereal, potatoes, molasses or apples.

Malt whisky

Malt whisky requires malted barley as its cereal component, and the first stage of production involves malting the barley to create enzymes that will convert the starch contained in the barley into soluble sugars.

This begins with what is termed 'steeping,' during which the barley is immersed in water several times, with 'air breaks' between immersions. This fools the barley into germinating much more quickly than it would in a field. In modern, commercial maltings, the barley is transferred into large metal drums, where air circulates in order to control the temperature of the grain. The next five days will see the barley sprout, and the skill of the maltster is to judge the precise point at which the cell walls have broken down and started to produce enzymes that will later convert starch to soluble sugars without using up all the starch, which would render it useless.

Germination is halted by a period of kilning, which involves heating and drying the barley – now known as 'green malt' – usually using gas, sometimes with the introduction of peat smoke if a peated style of malt is required.

Traditionally, the barley was laid out on malting floors at individual distilleries and turned manually, using wooden shovels, known as shiels, and coal and peat were employed for kilning. Ultimately, the sheer volume of malt required by expanding distilleries rendered most malting floors obsolete, and consistency was also an issue. However, this method is most likely to appeal to microdistillers wishing to make their own malt, particularly as consistency is not necessarily the overriding factor that it is for large-scale whisky makers.

Today, very few distillers make their own malt, though a handful of relatively large-scale commercial distillers in Scotland – including Balvenie, Highland Park, Laphroaig and Bowmore – produce a small proportion of their malt in-house, mixing it with malt bought in from commercial maltsters. The Islay 'farm' distillery of Kilchoman produces around 30 per cent of its own malt requirements and distils a 100 per cent Islay single malt using just barley grown on the distillery's own land and malted at the distillery.

A number of overseas microdistilling operations have chosen to make a virtue of malting their own barley to create the ultimate 'grain to glass' product, and it may be that as ever more UK distillers opt to distil whisky, some will follow that lead and develop maltings as a USP for their whisky.

Milling

Milling is usually the first stage of whisky making now undertaken at individual distilleries, and it serves to prepare the malt for mashing. A modern Buhler four row mill can process one tonne of malt per hour, grinding it into a coarse flour termed grist. This grist comprises three parts, namely husk, grits and flour. Proportions vary slightly from distillery to distillery, but a typical split would be in the region of 70 per cent grit, 20 per cent husk and 10 per cent flour. It is important to get this just right, as too fine a milling would be likely to clog up the mash tun, and too coarse a milling would allow the water – or liquor – to drain from the mash tun too quickly, without extracting the optimum amount of sugar.

Mashing

Mashing takes place in a mash tun, usually constructed from stainless steel and fully enclosed, though some older examples still found in distilleries are made from cast iron and are open-topped. A system of rakes or blades stir the mash for optimum extraction.

Most commercial whisky making distilleries are equipped with a circular mash tun with a conical top, and minimum capacity of 0.5 tonne or one tonne. However, for mashing on a relatively small scale, tuns with a less conventional appearance can be sourced. Jacketed, electric-heated mash tuns with a capacity of just 400 litres are available, though this style of tun also comes with larger dimensions, right up to 5,000 litres.

In a conventional mashtun, the grist is pumped into the vessel and hot water is added. The water acts with the enzymes developed during malting to convert starch into sugar. Strict temperature control is essential, as the enzymes will be killed if the water is too hot. The water is usually introduced at three or sometimes four stages, getting hotter each time, starting around 67°C and rising to near boiling point. Stirring the contents of the mash tun helps the drainage, sugar extraction and worts cloudyness – an important quality parameter. Once mashing is complete and no more sugar remains to be extracted, the wort – as it is called – is drained off through the vessel's perforated floor and cooled to between 16° C and 20° C prior to the fermentation stage of whisky production.

In smaller mash tuns, as described above, heating of the water takes place within the vessel, rather than being introduced from an external source.

Traditionally, the 'draff' or spent grain remaining in the mash tun after the wort has been drawn off has been in great demand as cattle food due to the high level of protein that it contains. This is obviously a very desirable state of affairs for the environmentally conscious microdistiller.

Fermentation

One cooled, wort is pumped into washbacks – or fermenters – for the fermentation stage of whisky-making. Traditionalists favour either larch or pine wood for washback construction, and a company like Joseph Brown Vats of Dufftown on Speyside (**www.woodenvats.com**) is highly skilled at fabricating wooden vessels such as these.

Those who advocate the continuing use of wooden washbacks rather than those made of stainless steel argue that the quality of spirit may be influenced by the activity of bacteria that the wood harbours, and which can never be totally eradicated, however vigorous the cleaning regime. One of the arguments for stainless steel is that backs made from the material are much easier to clean, and sterilisation is more complete.

Microdistillers tend to opt for stainless steel vessels – usually referred to as fermenters rather than washbacks – that essentially are cylindrical or conical tanks, with capacities varying from 200 to 5,000 litres. In the washback or fermenter, yeast is added to the cooled wort, the yeast cells multiply, feeding on the sugars, creating alcohol and carbon dioxide. The CO_2 causes the wash – as it is now officially known – to froth quite violently, and a rotating blade or 'switcher' is fitted in most washbacks to cut down the froth as it rises in the vessel.

The temperature of the wash increases – to a high of around 35° C, as does the level of alcohol present – to between six and nine per cent. The increasing alcohol level and lack of fermentable sugars causes yeast multiplication to be suppressed, and fermentation is effectively at an end after 48 hours.

Many distillers use this as their standard fermentation time, but others leave the wash in situ for more than twice that period, as secondary – bacterial – fermentation leads to sweeter, fruitier notes in the spirit finally distilled. Short fermentations tend to produce spirit with a nutty, spicy character.

Distillation

Distillation is the 'showbiz' end of whisky making, with its eye-catching still shapes and designs, and it is the stage where many permutations of equipment and operation come together to determine the character and quality of the whisky being made.

Conventional malt whisky distilling employs two – or occasionally three – connected copper pot stills, the first termed the wash still, and the second the spirit still.

The wash is pumped into the wash still and heated to around 78^0 C, at which point the alcohol boils and passes in vapour form from the still to a shell and tube condenser, or traditional worm tub – a long coil of copper immersed in a wooden or metal vessel containing cold water. In both cases, cold water turns the vapour into liquid, known as low wines, which has an alcohol strength of 20-23% ABV

The strength needs to be significantly increased, and this takes place in a spirit still, sometimes referred to as a low-wines still. Again, heat is applied to the still, and the early run of volatile compounds – known as foreshots – and the final run with its oily compounds – called feints – are kept separate from the heart of the run – the centre cut – that has a strength of around 68-70% ABV. This is collected in the spirit receiver, while the feints and foreshots are saved for re-distillation with the next fill of low wines.

Traditionally, the business of 'cutting' the spirit was done manually by a skilled stillman, using a hydrometer to measure specific gravity and a thermometer to gauge temperature in order to determine just when to cut. These calculations took place within a locked glass and brass-bound spirit safe to which the stillman had no access in order to maintain the level of security required by the excise service. The stillman cut the spirit by using external handles on the spirit safe to direct the liquid into either a receiver for feints and foreshots or a receiver for the heart of the run.

Today, many large-scale distilleries operate systems with programmable computerised cut points, and the stillman plays no creative part in the whisky-making process. Resident excisemen have long gone from individual distilleries too, and a regime of 'self-policing' means that the keys for the spirit safe locks are held by distillery management.

The microdistiller will, of course, be hands on when it comes to cutting spirit, and the points at which cuts are made varies in part on the style of spirit required. A broader cut is likely to be taken if a full-bodied, oily, even phenolic spirit is considered desirable.

As noted in Chapter Two, the shape and size of still are also important factors in the character of spirit produced. The key here is the amount of copper contact that the spirit experiences. As a rule of thumb, the more copper contact the lighter and 'cleaner' the spirit. A small, squat still does not allow for much copper contact, but a tall still allows for a significant degree of reflux – when vapour high in alcohol falls back down into the pot of the still for further distillation, exposing it to even more copper contact. The angle of the lyne arm or lye pipe which connects the still head to the condenser is also a factor in reflux, as an upwards sloping arm will encourage more of the vapour to fall back for further distillation, while a downwards sloping arm will have the opposite effect. Once collected, the spirit destined for maturation is reduced with water to an average filling strength of 63.5 per cent.

Not every whisky distiller uses a consecutive pot still distillation process, however, with some using the same still for both distillations, and others opting to pump wash into a 'beer stripping still,' more commonly used in Bourbon production in the USA. This produces low wines with a strength of around 85–90% ABV, and takes much less time than a pot still, also using only some 60 per cent of its energy requirements. If employing this method, the low wines are diluted with water before secondary distillation in a copper pot spirit still.

Other whiskies

The production process for pot still whiskies made from rye, or a combination of cereals such as wheat, barley and oats, are essentially the same as for malt whisky, though there may be some process differences due to the varying characteristics of the grains.

Vodka

If distilling from scratch using grain, the initial processes of vodka and gin production are very similar to those for making malt whisky. The grain is milled, mashed and fermented, and then sometimes run through a beer stripping still, as described above. The low wines may then be transferred to a copper pot still with an associated rectifying column for two consecutive distillations, further refining the spirit each time and diluting it with water between runs. When distillation is complete, the distiller draws off from the top of the column the foreshots or 'heads,' followed by the heart of the run and finally the feints or 'tails' fraction. To produce the purest vodka – which is actually ethanol plus water – distillers take a relatively narrow cut as the heart of the run. A final run to create the purest spirit possible may then be undertaken in a vodka 'polishing' column.

Other distillers will distil their vodka up to four times in a copper pot still and then run it twice though a rectifying column. The end result can be up to 96% ABV, though 80–85% ABV is more usual. This spirit is then reduced with pure water to bottling strength. Some distillation systems specifically designed to create vodka will comprise integrated copper pot, twin rectifying columns and a 'polishing' column. Another option is for vodka distillers to filter their product through carbon for ultimate purification, usually in a stainless steel vertical vessel known as a carbon column.

If distilling with potatoes or apples – in the manner of Chase Distillery – the potatoes or apples are initially mashed, and in the case of potatoes, brewer's yeast is added to encourage fermentation, while the apples will naturally ferment. The fermented liquid is then distilled in the same manner as cereals.

Gin

The method of gin distillation to the point where a pure spirit is created is identical to that of vodka. Indeed, many distillers use their vodka as the base for their gin. It is widely recognised that the size and shape of the still and the direction of lyne arm affect the character of gin just as much as they affect whisky. A short pot still with a downward-sloping lyne arm will produce a relatively oily, sweet gin, while a tall pot or a column still will lead to a 'cleaner' spirit.

The legal difference between vodka and gin is the use of botanicals to flavour the latter, with juniper being a compulsory ingredient. The botanicals are either fed into the still along with the spirit and redistilled (known as steeping or maceration) or placed in a basket at the head of the still (known as infusion). If using such a basket, the botanicals are assembled in a particular ratio by weight and layered according to particle size. The purpose of this distillation is to extract the essential oils from the botanicals, and these oils amount to less than five per cent of the total of botanicals used.

Where NGS has been bought in rather than distilled on site, the process of 'rectification' as it is known involves diluting the spirit to around 45% ABV before placing it and the botanicals in the still, or in a basket if infusion is preferred.

One notable still type once commonly used for infusion is the Carter Head still, developed during the 19th century by the Carter brothers, who worked for Aeneas Coffey before starting up their own still design and manufacturing enterprise. Their eponymous still was originally intended to rectify the crude spirit produced in Coffey stills into a spirit suitable for gin and vodka distillation. An average-sized Carter Head still usually has a capacity of around 3,000 litres and is fitted with a botanical basket.

Production of Carter Head stills ceased during the 1960s, but a number have been made since for gin distillation in the UK and abroad. A Carter Head still dating from 1948 is used in the production of Hendricks Gin, and Bombay Sapphire also employs one. Adnams Copper House distillery in Suffolk has an 850 litres copper pot still with a three-plate Carter Head for gin distillation, and when William Grant & Sons established their Reyka vodka distillery in Iceland in 2005, they had a bespoke Carter Head still with a high copper content constructed in order to produce a smooth vodka from just one distillation.

Whether steeping or infusion is practiced, once distillation is complete the gin is reduced to bottling strength (a minimum of 37.5% ABV, but usually stronger) using demineralised water.

If making 'London Dry' gin, no flavourings or colourings may be added after the distillation process, except for a tiny amount of sugar. This is the 'purest' form of gin and is intended to showcase the botanicals. 'Distilled gin' differs from London Dry in that flavourings may be added prior to bottling.

Making gin using the method known as 'compounding' is sometimes seen as a 'short-cut,' and lacking the integrity of rectification. Essentially, compounding involves extracting essential oils from botanicals by a process of pressing and then adding the oils to the neutral spirit.

Rum

Taking imported molasses as the starting point, the first stage of production is to ferment the molasses, in the same way that you would ferment grain. Distillation can take place in a pot still, column still or a hybrid combination of the two. The spirit collected after distillation will vary in strength from 70% ABV to 90% ABV, depending on the number of times it is distilled, and it is subsequently reduced with water to bottling strength.

Most rum is aged prior to bottling, using either ex-Bourbon casks or virgin oak casks. The effects are the same as when ageing any other spirit, with harsh elements being eliminated and new aromas and flavours created by the interaction between oak, spirit and air. As with whisky matured in a hot climate such as India or Australia, the effects are accelerated, and three years ageing in Goa or Tasmania may have much the same effect as 12 years in Speyside or County Cork.

Some rums will be infused with herbs, fruits or spices, and this process usually takes place after ageing. 'White rum' is filtered through charcoal to lighten the colour and flavour, producing a spirit more amenable to creating mixed drinks.

While most rum is made from molasses, a version known as 'rhum agricole' – originating in the French Caribbean – is produced by fermenting and distilling the juice pressed from sugar cane. It has quite intense flavours and is available in both unaged and aged versions.

There are four main production methods for rum made with molasses, namely distillation, maceration, infusion and percolation. Distillation usually takes place in a copper pot still, and the alcohol is mixed with the raw material in question and heated to extract flavour. Usually three runs are required to concentrate the flavours and remove impurities.

Maceration involves soaking the raw materials in spirit until their flavours are fully absorbed. The final product is known as 'tincture.' This may take up to a year, so patience is required! One way of speeding up the process is to undertake infusion, which involves heating the raw materials and spirit for several days.

The final method of percolation involves placing the materials in a container and bubbling heated spirit through it – much like the operation of a traditional coffee percolator. The end result is called 'extract.'

Whichever method is used, the resultant liquid is compounded to recipe specifications and then may be filled into oak casks to allow greater flavour development before being refined to remove impurities, filtered and mixed with sugar syrup to achieve the desired degree of sweetness. Vegetable dyes are used to add colour prior to a final filtering and bottling.

Case Study

Cotswolds Distillery
www.cotswoldsdistillery.com

The Cotswolds distillery is located in the Warwickshire village of Stourton, where New York-born former hedge fund manager Daniel Szor purchased Philip's Field Estate, complete with two stone buildings which were converted into a distillery and visitor centre. "I lived in Paris for 11 years and first got into whisky there, around 2000, through the Scotch Malt Whisky Society and La Maison du Whisky," he explains.

"The inspiration for the distillery came when I was looking out of the window of our farmhouse in the Cotswolds one summer day, watching growing spring barley, and I thought 'there's all this barley growing here, why is nobody making whisky with it?'"

"The Cotswolds attracts around 25 million people per year, and I figured they would provide a customer base for us, and I also took into consideration the burgeoning US craft distilling movement. Before we set up the distillery, I would go with friends to Scottish distilleries each year, and one we visited was Bruichladdich. We met the legendary distiller Jim McEwan there, and within 10 minutes he'd sold us a cask of whisky!"

Dan adds that "Jim encouraged me to follow my dream and put me in touch with Harry Cockburn, one-time manager of Bowmore, who works with start-up distillers across the globe. He helped to get the whole thing up and running, and the late Jim Swan was also invaluable for his knowledge of distilling chemistry and for creating a wood programme. Jim and Harry were both fantastic."

The whisky stills and associated equipment were supplied by Forsyth's of Rothes on Speyside, and are supplemented by a 1,200-litre hybrid pot and column gin still from Holstein. The first gin and single malt spirit flowed during 2014, with the latter being made from 100 per cent organic Cotswolds-grown barley.

Dan notes that "We use two main cask types of cask for maturation, namely first-fill Bourbon and 'STR.' The latter is an oak red wine cask, shaved, toasted and then charred. You get red fruit and berry notes, plus a lovely caramelised sugar character. The cask mix is 70 per cent STR and 30 per cent Bourbon, and this is our signature 'flagship' bottling going forward."

2016 saw the release of the distillery's first whisky, namely

Cotswolds Single Malt 2013 Harvest Organic Odyssey, followed in October 2017 by Cotswolds Single Malt Whisky. It is released in limited batches and bottled non-chill filtered. Each label lists the barley variety, harvest year and local Cotswolds farm on which it was grown.

In terms of funding, he notes that "I had enough money to purchase the property and the kit, but for operating capital we raised money from family and friends and two rounds of crowdfunding. We have 1,300 shareholders, and they are great brand ambassadors for us. In total, there is nearly £10 million invested in the venture. We expanded our operation by working two shifts per day, doubling production, and we can now make up to 130,000 litres per annum."

In addition to Cotswolds Dry Gin and Single Malt Whisky, Cotswolds distillery also produces 1616 Barrel Aged Gin, which is made by redistilling malt whisky in a pot still and combining it with juniper, coriander, nutmeg, orange peel and other botanicals. A third white spirit is named Hedgerow Gin, made by macerating local fruit and berries in Cotswolds Dry Gin for several months before it is slow-pressed, blended and lightly sweetened.

Dan Szor is keen to stress that most distillers need to increase production at some point, so it is sensible to start out with a relatively large capacity. "When we began distilling gin we expected to be using the Holstein still to make it perhaps a couple of times a month," he recalls, "but such was the demand that we found ourselves distilling 11 times a week and had to buy a bigger still – increasing from 500 litres to 1,200 litres."

In November 2018 a cask strength edition of Cotswolds single malt whisky was released under the Founder's Choice label, having been matured entirely in red wine barriques. According to Dan, "Beyond that, we're working on two whisky releases for autumn 2019, namely an Islay cask expression, aged full-term in Laphroaig quarter casks, and a sherry cask expression, matured in PX and Oloroso casks. In terms of the 'regular' single malt, we will gradually increase the age of the whisky to three to five years, and then five to seven, but we won't be using age statements."

Never one to rest on his laurels, Dan plans an intriguing addition to the Cotswolds' facilities. He explains that "Starting in the spring of 2019 we are going to build a distillery farm over two acres. We will create 56 individual beds in which we will grow botanicals and fruits, and we'll have an orchard, with apples, pears and plums."

Cider brandy

The production of cider brandy parallels that of other spirits at the distillation stage. It takes approximately 11 litres of cider to make one litre of spirit and seven tonnes of apples to fill a small barrel for maturation. Ageing the spirit is key to creating something really fine, and the interaction between oak casks and the atmosphere has just as significant an effect on cider brandy as it does on whisky.

Bottling and packaging

Even the most cursory glance at the shelves of any spirits retailer – physical or virtual – will reveal how hard producers strive to differentiate their brands from those of competitors. As the marketplace for microdistilled spirits becomes ever more crowded, making your own product stand out has never been more important.

The two most obvious ways of doing this are by bottle and label design, and the good news is that professional help is available when it comes to this crucial aspect of marketing, with many distillery consultants available, at a fee, to offer their expertise. Bear in mind that the way your spirit is presented reflects your own values, aspirations and ethics, and will be extrapolated into supporting marketing materials, and even into your distillery visitor experience if you have one. Getting it right is crucial.

Before deciding on bottling and packaging solutions it is probably wise to know how much you want to sell your spirits for, factoring their potential cost into overall calculations. Nobody wants to see profit margins reduced significantly, however artistic and eye-catching the presentation appears!

Another factor to bear in mind is the overall weight of your product, which could have a bearing on distribution, and also its desirability to overseas visitors whose luggage may already be bulging with heavy items. One single malt Scotch brand that shall remain nameless launched new release a few years ago in a high-quality, heavy bottle fitted into a wooden casket, and accompanied by a slab of genuine Scottish limestone. It looked extremely impressive but shouted to the traveller 'excess baggage.'

Bottles

It is possible to have your own bottle designed from scratch, a process that involves initially creating a 3D design image, allowing the manufacturer to calculate thickness and the overall amount of glass or crystal required for the project. Beyond that, a mould is created before production can commence. All of this costs money, but also time. If you have a specific launch date in mind, you may want to allow up to six months for a bottle-making company to come up with the goods

As suggested above, there is a choice between using glass or crystal for your bottle, whether bespoke or selected from an existing design already in production. Crystal is heavier and costlier, and with a more traditional luxury perception, this may not necessarily chime with the ethos of your product.

When it comes to closures, screw-tops definitely do not have connotations of craft and provenance, so the extra cost of stopper corks is well worth paying.

Labelling

However you wish your label or labels to look, there is a certain amount of information that they are legally required to carry. This information includes a 'duty-paid' stamp, ideally included on a back label, expression of volume in cubic litres, strength expressed as % vol. alcohol, country of origin, and any required product description, such as 'Scotch Malt Whisky.' It is also advisable to include a health warning about drinking sensibly.

Decide how much information you want to impart via the packaging. Too much looks cluttered – clean lines are good – but then again, your product may not be known to the potential consumer compared to the likes of Gordon' Gin, Johnnie Walker Whisky or Smirnoff Vodka, all of which are familiar and trusted brands. You should try to get your USP or USPs across on the packaging if at all possible.

Using a carton or tube to hold your bottle allows space for additional information that will not fit onto the bottle labels, and has connotations of a quality product, but it will, of course, add to your costs, and with environmental issues such as recycling likely to be of importance to your target market, many microdistillers prefer to allow their bottles to do the talking without further embellishment. Details of designers, and bottle and label manufacturers are listed on page 149.

Contract bottling

Initially, it may well be worthwhile investing in some small-scale bottling machinery to handle relatively low volumes, but as your business grows, it could pay dividends to have your spirits contract-bottled by a third party.

A company such as H&A Prestige Bottling Ltd **www.hacontractbottling.co.uk** based in Lancashire – operates 11 bottling lines and handles everything from 3cl to 4.5 litre bottles. Not only does the firm offer bottling facilities, but it also provides guidance to ensure compliance with domestic and export legislation and packaging solutions, relating to capping and corking, labelling, case and carton design and bar-coding. Other contract bottlers are listed in Appendix on page 147.

On-site bottling

One option for the start-up distiller is hand-bottling and labelling, but this is a time-consuming – and arguably soul-destroying – task. A company such as Chromex Technology Ltd **www.chromextech.com** offers a semi-automatic benchtop single head filling machine, which is a cost-effective piece of kit for the microdistiller, while a four-head filler from the likes of Vigo Ltd **www.vigoltd.com** should be able to handle around 500 bottles per hour. Second-hand bottling and labelling equipment can be sourced from a number of UK companies, including Perry Process Equipment **www.perryprocess.co.uk** and SC Packaging Technology **www.sc-packaging.com**, as well as manufacturers and retails of new kit, such as Aco Packaging Ltd **www.acosales.co.uk** and Enterprise Tondelli **www.enterprisetondelli.co.uk.** Other suppliers of bottling, labelling and closure equipment are listed on page 149.

Quality control

Although the hands-on distiller should recognise any deviations in quality and consistency from one batch of spirit to another, assembling a small 'tasting panel' of trusted individuals who are very familiar with the product or products in question is a good way of backing up the individual's judgement. Involving staff members and/or supporters in a tasting panel is also a good way of making them feel valued and their abilities respected.

'Control' samples of the optimum character required should also be retained and compared to future production to ensure there is no gradual 'drift' in quality or style. As well as organoleptic assessments, gas chromatography analysis can be invaluable to ensure that all batches of spirit meet the required specification, therefore ensuring consistency.

When ageing gin, vodka, rum or whisky in casks, the business of quality control becomes more difficult, as each cask interacts with the spirit it contains in subtly different ways. There is no absolute constant, and larger scale distillers blend numbers of casks together for greater consistency between batches. This is not necessarily an option for the microdistiller, and his or her intention may, at any rate, be to celebrate the individuality of casks by bottling them separately. Consistency is not necessarily essential, but quality is.

Remember, the chances are that your customer base will probably be relatively local and also more than usually knowledgeable. Consumers are also likely to be enthusiastic users of social media and will not be slow to make negative posts relating to products they consider lacking in quality. First and foremost, however, quality – and associated integrity – should be at the heart of all microdistilling enterprises. If 'small' isn't necessarily good, then why shop 'small'?

Chapter Four
Financing a distillery

Writing a business plan demonstrates a serious statement of intent and forces would-be distillers to focus on all aspects of the operation they plan to create. Frequently, its composition causes the author(s) to address issues to which they had not previously given consideration. The plan should cover objectives, strategies, sales, marketing and financial forecasts. It will show a real understanding of the prevailing spirits markets and how the new business is expected to perform, typically on a one to three year basis.

A business plan will be required by any organisation to which application is made to borrow funds, and will help to reassure other investors, such as family and friends, that their money appears to be in good hands. It is also a legal requirement by HMRC if the intention is to use a still of less than 18 hectolitres capacity, and, as HMRC guidelines note, "A business plan can help assure us of your suitability for approval, particularly if you are a new distiller without previous or existing licences."

Apart from such formal requirements, however, a business plan shows that this is not a casual hobby, but hopefully a productive and professional venture worthy of respect and consideration by all of those involved, including customers, suppliers and potential employees.

Base the plan on detailed information, but do not go into too much detail. Keep it simple, clear and readable, and present it in a professional manner. It is important to include CVs of key personnel associated with the business in an appendix. This is particularly important if seeking external funding.

The business and products

Where relevant, explain the history of the business, when it started trading, what progress has been made to date and the structure of ownership.

Describe your products, avoiding jargon and overly-technical statements, and outline how you intend to develop the business.

Provide an overview of the British distilling industry, and the size and relevance of microdistilling as part of that.

Note key competitors, their market shares, along with your own market share or target share, and outline how your products differ from theirs in terms of price, quality, distribution and points of uniqueness.

Identify characteristics of customers within the microdistilling sector and an analysis of your own existing customer base, where possible. Outline trends within the sector and identify likely future trends.

Sales and marketing

- The most important part of the business plan is where you intend to place your products in the market, describing any unique selling features and how you plan to exploit them. Stress that in the world of microdistilling, provenance and authenticity are extremely important, and that your products will be priced to reflect their exclusivity. Identify area where profits will be made.
- Identify how you intend to market your products. Will your distillery have visitor facilities and tour options, spirit masterclasses or 'schools,' plus a retail area? If so, how much of your revenue is likely to come through direct product sales and monies generated by on-site activities? What is the value of this personal interface in terms of creating brand loyalty, and what are the associated costs of running such an operation?
- How do you plan to let potential consumers know what is on offer at the distillery and details of your products? Are you intending to employ a PR company or appoint an individual to cover this aspect of the business?
- Engaging with local tourist organisations is an important way of achieving brand exposure, and the value of providing information leaflets – perhaps with discount vouchers – to be placed in visitor packs at accommodation sites and other venues should not be underestimated.
- Reassure readers of your business plan that you understand the importance of the internet and social media. A well designed and high quality website that is easy to navigate is invaluable in terms of creating and raising the profile of the business and its products, and also as what may be your premier sales outlet.
- The likes of Facebook, Instagram and Twitter are extremely useful for generating interest in your products, and such channels should be exploited by whoever is handling your PR activities.
- Explain routes to market other than direct sales from your venue or by ecommerce. Will you also be selling through wholesalers or individual retail outlets? What is the timescale for making sales and receiving payment. What is the rate of repeat business and what is the average sales value?

Staffing

Clarify staffing requirements in production, sales, marketing, finance and administration, and outline recruitment and training plans with costings and timescales. Compare the efficiency of your staff with those of competitors, in terms of sales, salaries and retention rates. Staff members should be motivated and incentivised. Stress your own commitment to the business by revealing your financial investment.

Operational activities

Detail your operational equipment, noting its value, its life expectancy and the need to upgrade or expand. Similarly, consider the property in which your business is based. Is it an extension of an existing agricultural or brewing enterprise? Is there scope for expansion on the present site, or would expansion necessitate a move? Are there specific advantages or disadvantages to the premises in question? How do you select and monitor suppliers of key ingredients such as cereal, NGS, bottles and closures?

Reassure readers of your business plan that reliable and flexible management information systems are in place, regarding sales, accounts and stock control. A reliable IT system is essential. Include details of regulatory and quality standards to which the business conforms.

Financial forecasts

For an existing business, the plan should include information relating to trading during the past three to five years, but for start-up businesses without such data it is a case of providing forecasts for the same period going forwards.

Provide profit and loss, cash flow and sales projections, and in some cases balance sheet forecasts may also be required. Back up the projections with your reasoning behind these figures to reassure readers that this is not just wishful thinking or numbers plucked out of the air. For example, if the business arena in which you operate is becoming increasingly competitive, then it may be necessary to predict narrower profit margins than might otherwise be the case. Always be realistic about the figures you provide.

Detailed financial forecasts are best included in an appendix to avoid cluttering the main pages of the plan. Include anticipated individual product profit margins, timescale of payment from debtors, extent of credit offered to you by suppliers and the amount of finance you expect to receive and interest rates to be paid on that finance where appropriate. If external funding by bank loan is part of your model, allow a contingency of 10 to 20 per cent on your funding requirements.

In some cases, banks or local business support organisations will aid the production of financial forecasts without charge, and the National Enterprise Network **www.nationalenterprisenetwork.org** in England and Scottish Enterprise **www.scottish-enterprise.com** in Scotland offer impartial, independent advice on financing and all other aspects of starting up a business. Similarly, trade associations such as the Wine & Spirit Trade Association **www.wsta.co.uk** can often offer invaluable information specific to the microdistilling industry, with existing members frequently being keen to share advice on the 'dos and don'ts' of starting out.

Does it all add up?

A simple exercise in SWOT analysis (strengths, weaknesses, opportunities and threats) can be a valuable way of testing the credibility in your business plan.

Strengths may include the uniqueness and quality of products, the experience of the management team and workforce, the brand name and presentation and even the ability to finance the venture without external borrowing and consequent interest payments.

Weaknesses may include excessive reliance on external funding, a narrow customer base or lack of management experience in the microdistilling sector.

Opportunities may include growing demand within the sector or the exit of key competitors.

Threats may include a decline in demand or the entry of an ambitious rival with similar products in the sector.

Declare in realistic terms the anticipated status of the business in three years' time and set specific targets within that timeframe. Outline key objectives, such as launching new products, generating a higher level of sales, increasing profit margins, growing your customer base, encouraging a greater volume of repeat business, upskilling your employees and recruiting new ones with specialist skills and experience. Create an action plan to detail how you will achieve the objectives as outlined.

Obtaining a licence to rectify or distil

HM Revenue and Customs (HMRC) is the organisation responsible for licencing all British distilleries. At the heart of its activities is the existence of Spirits Duty, "Payable on any spirits, or any mixture or combination of spirits with anything else, at a strength of more than 1.2% alcohol by volume (ABV). Spirits are liable for Spirits Duty as soon as they've been manufactured."

The current relevant legislation (as of January 2018) is set out in Excise Notice 39: spirits production in the UK **www.gov.uk/government/ publications/excise-notice-39-spirits-production-in-the-uk/excise-notice-39-spirits-production-in-the-uk** for further information.

The main legal provisions relating to the production of spirits and spirits rectifiers and compounders are to be found in Alcoholic Liquor Duties Act 1979, Spirits Regulations 1991 and Spirits (Amendment) Regulations 2013.

Also relevant to spirits producers and spirits rectifiers and compounders are The Customs and Excise Management Act 1979 and The Revenue Traders (Accounts and Records) Regulations 1992, while product-specific legislation is contained in The Scotch Whisky Regulations 2009.

Excise Notice 39 notes that "The same general requirements and conditions will apply at all spirits production premises, whether spirits production comes from fermented cereals, from fermented molasses, by 'cracking' ethylene gas or by any other process. This notice mainly focuses on the end-to-end process of spirits production, from the application process to production and warehousing, and payment of duty."

Responsibilities

The Notice explains that "You must exercise control over all aspects of your spirits production including:
- The physical security of your premises, plant or vessels
- The security of spirits produced
- Accurately accounting for the spirits produced
- Rendering returns on time
- Examining losses and identifying their cause
- Investigating any irregularity at your premises
- Implementing and monitoring reasonable and effective measures to prevent any loss of dutiable spirits

You should make sure your procedures and records for production and stock control take these aspects into account."

The application process for new distillers

According to Excise Notice 39, "As a new distiller, there can be a lot to consider before production begins. The table below provides an overview of the steps you need to take before you can start production. Detailed guidance follows on what you need to do, how and when to do it. Please note, this describes the route of a successful application.

Stage	Action	Notes
Preparation	Prepare a business plan	Identify production and warehouse premises: if not yet purchased, you'll need evidence that you're planning their purchase
	1. Apply for or obtain a distiller's licence (DLA1)	You may need to apply for a letter of indication of likely approval to satisfy bank lending requirements, for example
	2. Apply for or obtain an approval of plant and process	You may need to apply for a letter of indication of likely approval to satisfy bank lending requirements, for example
Application (at least 45 days before production begins)	3. Gain approval for a warehouse to hold spirits (EX69) and gain authorisation as a warehousekeeper	See Excise Notice 196 for information on the requirements to provide a financial guarantee for the warehousing of produced spirits, and registration as owner of goods in a third party warehouse, depending on your circumstances
	Where appropriate, register for the Alcohol Wholesaler Registration Scheme (Excise Notice 2002)	If you plan to sell alcohol to other businesses
	Where appropriate, apply for verification under the Spirit Drink Verification scheme	If you'll be producing Scotch whisky, Irish whiskey, cream or poitin or Somerset cider brandy

When all licences and approvals have been received by the applicant, production can begin."

Before applying to HMRC

Identify production and warehouse premises. If you don't own these, you'll need to provide evidence to show you are planning to purchase them with any application you make.

Note that any variations between initial proposals and final plans could lead to a delay or rejection of your application.

At least 45 days before you start to produce spirits:

Use form DLA1, Alcohol duties: application for a distiller's licence and approval of distillery plant and process to apply.

Alongside your DLA1 form, provide us with the required information to seek approval of plant and process.

We can issue a letter of indication to help you in securing finance to complete your plans where we're satisfied from the details in your application that you are likely to succeed.

We'll only issue the final distiller's licence when we're satisfied that all necessary requirements are in place, including premises security.

Use form:

- EX61 to apply for authorisation as a warehousekeeper
- EX69 to apply for approval to operate an excise warehouse

If you wish to store spirits in a third-party warehouse. Apply for registration as an owner of warehoused goods using form EX60 – Excise warehousing: application to be an owner of duty-suspended goods held in excise warehouses

Please note that 45 working days is the standard time taken to process applications. The actual time taken to process applications depends on the circumstances of each individual applicant. For example, if you've not provided all the required information or the application refers to premises that require building work, the time taken to process and approve the application may be longer than 45 days.

Once you've received your:

- distiller's licence
- approval of plant and process
- proper warehouse and warehousekeeper approvals

You are then ready to begin to produce spirits."

Plant and process

At the same time as you apply for a distiller's licence, you must apply for approval of the plant and process you intend to use. The following information is required by HMRC:

- Address of proposed distillery
- Plan of premises
- Full description of the manufacturing process, including size of still
- The number and description of the vessels used in the manufacturing process, their capacity and use of all plant
- Your intended source of raw materials and the range of products you intend to produce

• Where the product will be stored, including security arrangements

According to HMRC, "We may refuse to issue a licence where the largest still to be used has a capacity below 18 hectolitres. However, we'll consider applications for a distiller's licence providing you use the still for the commercial production of spirits. You must submit a business plan to support your application for commercial production.

If you intend to produce a UK spirit drink with a protected Geographical Indication (GI) you must apply for verification under HMRC's Spirit Drinks Verification Scheme in addition to the process described above for obtaining a distiller's licence and approval of plant and process. The current spirit drinks with protected GI status in the UK are Scotch whisky, Irish whiskey, cream and poitin, and Somerset cider brandy.

"We'll only grant approval to applicants who can demonstrate that they are fit and proper to carry on a controlled activity. This means HMRC must be satisfied the business is genuine and that all persons with an important role or interest in it are law abiding, responsible and don't pose any significant threat in terms of potential revenue non-compliance or fraud."

Security

As the licence-holder, you are responsible for the security of the spirit until duty is paid. HMRC will check to make sure your security systems protect the revenue. You must pay duty on any losses you can't explain.

"The list gives some ideas of what we would normally expect.

Area	Security must include	Regularly demonstrated by
Distillery site	Perimeter and building security that deters casual entry and identifies signs of forced entry	Security reviews
Still room and distiller's warehouse	Regular checks of vessels and plant and have restricted access	Management checks to ensure any lapses in security are put right
Vessels and plant	Measures to secure all vessel openings are locked or sealed and that signs of tampering or pilferage don't go unnoticed	Security reviews and management checks
	Technology of a high standard that controls access to all areas and vessels on the site	

We expect all plant to be:
• Accessible
• Readily identifiable
• With the exception of working stills, capable of being opened as required for our inspection
and that all:
• Wash backs
• Feints receivers
• Spirit receivers
are gauged and calibrated, with calibration tables readily available.

There's no requirement to mark particular items, however we expect the use of plant and vessels to be identifiable in your business records."

In production

Excise Notice 39 states that "Distillation periods are accounting periods for the manufacture of spirits. You must carry out all manufacturing in these periods. A period is usually between a week and a month. You must specify the start and finish dates of each period in your records. If you manufacture more than one class of spirits, you must specify separate periods for each class of spirit. These periods may run simultaneously.

Every distillation period should be clearly identifiable in your business records.

Until you've taken separate accounts, you mustn't mix spirits produced in different periods."

Eight 'classes of spirits' are identified by HMRC, namely:
1) Malt spirits
2) Grain spirits
3) Neutral spirits of agricultural origin
4) Neutral spirits of non-agricultural origin
5) Spirits produced from beer
6) Spirits produced from wine or made-wine
7) Spirits produced from cider or perry
8) Other

Notice 39 states that "You may take duty-unpaid samples of wort, wash, feints and spirits for the purposes of:
• Quality control
• Strength testing

- Scientific research
- Reference
- Other production-related analysis

However, you must:

- Note the samples taken in your business records
- Keep the quantity to the minimum necessary for the purpose
- Label the samples as 'sample'
- Label samples of spirits, 'duty-unpaid sample – not for sale'
- Destroy samples no longer required
- Keep records of their use and disposal

You may receive and store in duty suspense, wash and feedback from the premises of a:

- Registered cider maker
- Licensed wine producer
- Registered brewer

providing your premises are covered by an excise warehouse approval."

Measuring wort, wash, gravity & alcoholic strength

According to HMRC, "You must keep an accurate record of the quantity and gravity of wort and wash collected. The quantity and gravity of wort and wash should be measured using recognised industry methods. You should use any industry-recognised equipment, in accordance with the manufacturer's protocol.

Automatic densimeters must measure density according to regulation 18 of the Spirits Regulations 1991. The automatic densimeter must carry out density measurements with accuracy and precision. All of the approved densimeters have been 5 decimal place machines, and when used according to the operator's instructions, have proved to be accurate and precise enough for our purposes."

Warehousing

Regulations state that "You must immediately warehouse all spirits once you've established the quantity produced (known as 'taking account'). Distillers may store spirits produced in their own distillery, known as a 'distiller's warehouse.'

Excise duty

"Excise Duty becomes chargeable following distillation

or manufacture of spirits in any other way. It's not normally payable until the spirits are taken out of warehouse storage. We may ask you to pay duty on any losses, which occur at your distillery or while transferring spirits to a warehouse, which are not due to natural wastage or for which you don't have an acceptable explanation."

The 'Duty Charge' is normally based on the litres of alcohol contained in the spirits and any feints produced, less the litres of alcohol in any feints brought forward from the previous period. This is known as the actual charge.

GI

Certain UK spirit drinks, for example, Scotch whisky, are protected under EU legislation as a product of 'GI,' or 'Geographical Indication.'

HMRC is the designated verifying authority for UK spirit drinks with a protected GI. If you produce a UK GI spirit drink, you must apply to HMRC for verification of your processes.

Age and origin

Certificates of age and origin attest to the authenticity of UK-produced spirits. HMRC issues these to support exporters and producers of UK-manufactured spirits and facilitate entry of their product into overseas markets.

The majority of issued certificates are in respect of Scotch whisky exports. The certificates are an essential part of the industry's efforts to protect Scotch whisky in overseas markets from counterfeiting.

According to HMRC, "We issue certificates of age and origin to UK applicants who are able to provide a satisfactory audit trail of the origin of the product. This is restricted to distillers and brand owners and manufacturers and holders of goods in duty-suspense.

We may also issue certificates of age and origin to overseas applicants for spirits previously consigned that are being sent on to a further overseas destination (for example, from UK to France to Taiwan), providing the applicant provides a certificate of non-manipulation and also holds satisfactory documentary evidence of the spirits' origin.

There's a charge for certificates – and you need to contact by email: **certificates.sdvs@hmrc.gsi.gov.uk**."

Spirits rectifiers and compounders
HMRC Excise Notice 39:

	Rectifer	Compounder
Definition	You're a rectifier if you re-distil spirits (with or without flavouring ingredients)	You're a compounder if you combine or mix plain spirits or previously compounded spirits with any other substance, except water, so as to distinctly alter the character or flavour of the plain spirits or compounded spirits, producing a new compounded spirit
When do I need a licence?	You must hold a rectifier's licence if you are a rectifier or compounder and keep a still to carry out either process	You must hold a compounder's licence if: you don't have a rectifier's licence and you manufacture (by compounding) alcoholic liquors other than mixed drinks and 'coolers' that are made-wines as defined by the Alcoholic Liquor Duties Act 1979, ingredients (for example, essences, bitters) for incorporation in alcoholic liquors (either in their manufacture or as a mixer)
When don't I need a licence?	Not applicable. You'll always need a licence to rectify (including for own use)	If you're compounding in a still and have a rectifier's licence, or if you compound spirits solely in order to make: foodstuffs produced solely for consumption on the premises food products, such as liqueur chocolates or the liquid fillings that are put into them flavouring essences of the type used solely in confectionery or other food, mineral waters or medicines perfumes if you're compounding spirits for your own use
What warehouse facility do I need?	For duty-suspended spirits, approved trade facility warehouse	For duty-suspended spirits, approved trade facility warehouse
	For duty-paid spirits, none	For duty-paid spirits, none

You apply for a rectifier's or compounder's licence by completing form L5, Alcohol duties: application for a licence to carry on an Excise Trade. There's no charge for the licence.

Alcohol Wholesaler Registration Scheme (AWRS)

If you sell alcohol to another business you may need to apply to register for the Alcohol Wholesaler Registration Scheme (AWRS).

HMRC states that "You must have a valid Government Gateway User ID and password. If you don't have an account you'll need to create a Government Gateway account.

To verify your business details, we'll try to match them to an HM Revenue and Customs (HMRC) record that holds your Unique Taxpayer Reference (UTR).

This will be your:

- Corporation Tax UTR as a limited company
- Self Assessment UTR for any type of partnership
- Individual Self Assessment UTR as a self employed or sole trader

You can apply for approval as a:

- Limited company
- Sole trader/self-employed
- Business partnership
- Limited liability partnership
- Limited partnership
- Group

As a new business, you may have to provide additional information after applying. You would usually supply this during your site visit and it would include:

- Your business plan
- Letters of intent from suppliers and customers
- Third-party distribution companies

All businesses that supply alcohol to other businesses for resale need to apply. This includes:

- Breweries and microbreweries
- Wine producers and vineyards
- Spirit producers
- Cider producers who make more than 70 hectolitres of cider a year
- Wine importers
- General wholesalers selling alcohol, including cash and carry businesses
- Specialist wine wholesalers

Before you start

Make sure you have all the information you'll need before you begin to apply online. As well as the relevant UTR and your Government

CASE STUDY

ADNAMS
www.adnams.co.uk

Adnams Sole Bay brewery in Southwold, Suffolk, was established in 1872 by George and Ernest Adnams. Having grown from its East Anglian base into a nationally recognised brewing company, the former Copper House at Sole Bay was given a new lease of life, when it was converted into a distillery during 2009/10, after a new brewhouse had been installed.

According to the company, "Adnams is the first brewery/distillery (a bristillery?!) in England that's able to produce high-quality spirits directly from malted grains all the way through to the finished product. We use the same local ingredients to make our spirits – barley, rye, wheat and oats – as we do for our beers."

Adnams claims that Copper House is the most energy-efficient distillery in the UK, and it also generates water and steam for the brewery, "forming an integral part of our overall sustainable production system."

Distilling equipment was sourced from Carl GmbH in Germany, and Corporate and Communications Manager Sarah Fisk explains that the distillery is equipped with "A continuous beer stripping column, a pot still connected to rectifying columns with an additional de-meth column for vodka production, a Carter-head pot still for gin production and an alembic-head pot still for whisky production. The washes we use are produced by the brewery and then pumped to the distillery when ready. They are all bespoke recipes."

She adds that "We didn't take on specialist distilling staff originally, our distiller came from Engineering, but as we've grown we now have a team in the distillery as we operate 24 hours a day. We have capacity for approximately 200,000lpa, split 50/50 gin/whisky."

Adnams uses locally grown barley, wheat and oats in the production of its whiskies, vodkas and gins, and also makes Rising Sun Gin, Rye Hill Vodka and Rye Single Malt whisky using rye.

Sarah Fisk says that "We like to create premium, great tasting products with good provenance. Our Chairman, Jonathan Adnams, grows rye just a couple of miles away from the distillery, so apart from creating great tasting vodka and whisky, we're able to talk about the provenance of the grain, too."

Inevitably, having a long-established and highly-regarded drinks business behind you is a major advantage when it comes to venturing into distilling, as the abundance of rules and regulations and necessity of keeping highly efficient records does not come as a shock. There is also the singular plus that routes to market are already well-established and wide-reaching, with Adnams not only having an estate of managed and independently-run on-trade licensed premises, but also several branded retail outlets and a thriving online trade.

"We have the benefit of an existing strong brand name in the drinks market," say Sarah Fisk. "We're already known and trusted by consumers and so they are willing to try our new spirits. Our experience and knowledge of brewing and the various grains and ingredients is also hugely beneficial.

"Export is relatively new market for us, both with beer and spirits. It is a challenge for any business but having a varied and great quality product range makes entry into new markets slightly easier. There are so many small brands on the market now, and it grows almost daily, so one of the biggest challenges is the amount of competition."

In terms of getting the word out about its products, Adnams values social media very highly, as do most of its competitors. "Social media is really important to us," says Fisk. "It has so many formats and is a great way of engaging with customers. You can react quickly unlike many other forms of promotion or advertising."

From the start of its distilling venture, Adnams has been keen to expand the range of English whiskies available, as well as producing white spirits, and in 2013 Copper House released Single Malt No. 1 – a three-year-old matured in new French oak barrels – and Triple Grain No. 2 – made from malted barley, wheat and oats, and aged in new American oak casks. The company's whisky portfolio now includes a Single Malt aged for four years in new French oak barrels, a Rye Malt Whisky made from 75 per cent rye and 25 per cent barley and matured for a minimum of five years in new French oak, and five-year-old Triple Malt Whisky, distilled from barley, wheat and oats, and aged in new American oak barrels.

Additionally, the firm produces Adnams Spirit of Broadside, described as an 'eau de vie de biere,' distilled from the brewery's best-selling dark ruby Broadside beer and matured in heavily-toasted Russian Oak casks for 12 months.

Gateway details, you may need the following information:
- Your VAT number and company registration number (if you have one)
- The addresses of your additional trading premises
- For UK residents – the names and National Insurance numbers of all business directors, company secretaries or partners
- For non-UK residents – the names and passport numbers of all business directors, company secretaries or partners
- The names, addresses and VAT registration numbers of up to five of your largest alcohol suppliers, by volume (if you have suppliers)

You might also have to tell us about:
- The products you sell
- The types of customer you have
- How you take orders

Applying online to register for the AWRS service

You must apply giving notice of at least 45 calendar days. This will allow HMRC to process your application and undertake the fit and proper test. You'll get an acknowledgement with a reference number of your application. You must wait until you get approval from HMRC before you start trading."

Duty stamps

The UK Duty Stamps Scheme applies to bottles and other retail containers of spirits, and wine or made-wine with an alcohol by volume of 30 per cent or more, in bottle sizes of 35 centilitres or more.

By law, if you import or make these types of products that are intended for consumption in the UK, you'll need to affix a duty stamp or include one on your label. It's free to register and get duty stamps.

The duty stamp is available in two formats:

A product specific stamp (referred to in the law as a type A stamp) to be attached directly to the bottle, known as free-standing stamps

A stamp (referred to in the law as a type B stamp) incorporated into bottle labels and printed by the industry's own label printers, known as label stamps.

Each free-standing stamp has a unique number printed on the face. This number contains a letter identifier, which denotes the product type. For example, W50000012345 is a free-standing stamp for whisky/whiskey. Free-standing stamps are available showing

the following product types:
- Whisky/whiskey (W)
- Gin (G)
- Vodka (V)
- Rum (R)
- Brandy (B)
- Other product (P)

The product type on the free-standing stamp must refer to the description of the contents of the bottle to which it's attached. Each separate label design features a unique reference number to identify the person to whom it was issued.

Applications

Firstly, you need to register with HMRC for the scheme, and you can do this online. Alternatively you can download from **www.gov. uk/guidance/duty-stamps-scheme-how-to-register**.
- You'll need to provide:
- Your name and address
- Your legal status
- Your UK VAT registration number (if you have one)
- Your Excise ID number (if you have one)
- How many free-standing stamps you expect to order in the next 12 months (if any)
- How many free-standing stamps you would have needed in the previous year
- The name and address of the label printer(s) that you'll use for label stamps.

HMRC will acknowledge receipt of your application and issue a registration letter to you, containing your registration number. When you've received your registration number you can request the stamps.

With your registration number, you'll receive details of HMRC's label stamps design contractor. You'll need to order the design specification for the label stamp from them, including:
- Your duty stamps registration number
- The number of copies of the design specification that you need
- Details of where the design specification should be delivered.

The contractor will confirm receipt of your order and arrange for the design to be sent to you.

Shortly after your registration number arrives, you'll receive another letter from HMRC with website details of the contractor that supplies freestanding stamps. You can order your stamps

through the website. You'll need to provide:
- Your duty stamps registration number
- The number of stamps you need for each product type
- The address of the premises where the stamps are to be affixed
- The name and address of the person who will be affixing the stamps (if not the registered person)
- The address of the premises where the goods will be held until they have stamps affixed to them (if you're bringing unstamped goods into the UK and you're not holding them in an excise warehouse).

In most cases you can choose whether to use free-standing or label stamps according to your individual circumstances. If you're an authorised warehousekeeper, a registered consignee, a registered commercial importer or a tax representative you may order label stamps as well as free-standing stamps.

Other information

Labels that incorporate duty stamps must also show one of the following:

In an easily legible form, a brand under which it's intended that the alcoholic liquor will be sold by retail
- The trademark of the product contained in the bottle
- Details of the producer
- Details of the business marketing the product

It is also a legal requirement to provide a batch core number that allows traceability back to the spirit batch that was bottled. While not a legal requirement the distiller should retrain a production sample labelled so that it can be traced to the bottling batch. These are invaluable should any dispute arise with a customer over the bottled contents.

Accounts, records and duty payments

According to HMRC, "The following requirement has the force of law and is made under regulation 6 of the Revenue Traders (Accounts and Records) Regulations 1992.

You must keep a record of the spirits you've produced. The record must include the:
- Date and time
- Spirits receiver or other vessel
- Dip or gauge reading
- Temperature and hydrometer readings
- Quantity of spirits, adjusted to a temperature of 20°C, with

details of bulk volume, strength and litres of alcohol produced. Information is also required on processes and operations such as:

- fermentations
- distillations, including the start and finish of each distillation period and any process or stage of the process in the manufacture of spirits
- deliveries to warehouse

Your normal business records should be enough, but we may ask you to modify them if needed. There's no prescribed format and records may be electronic or written – but they must be:

- Accurate and kept up-to-date
- Readily accessible to us
- Kept for at least six years from the date of the last entry.

Your records must be available for inspection at all reasonable times. You must keep all records and documents relating to:

- Stock
- Handling
- Purchases
- Sales
- Imports
- Exports
- Yeast slurry.

In addition, we may also wish to look at:

- Profit and loss and trading statements
- Management accounts and reports
- Balance sheets
- Internal and external auditors' reports
- Any record maintained for a business purpose.

We're aware that much of the information we have access to is confidential and we'll take great care to respect your confidentiality. Any incidents that affect operations, for example a breakdown of plant, must be recorded accurately in your business records.

You need to complete a quarterly distillery production return – form W21 – at the end of March, June, September and December each year. You'll need to complete a return for each different class of spirit you distil.

In order to pay Excise Duty on spirits held in an excise warehouse, you, as the warehousekeeper, must complete either form W5 or form W5D. Alternatively you can use the Alcohol and Tobacco Warehousing Declarations (ATWD) online service **www.gov.uk/ guidance/alcohol-and-tobacco-warehousing-declarations**.

CASE STUDY

EAST LONDON LIQUOR COMPANY
www.eastlondonliquorcompany.com

The East London Liquor Company was founded in 2013 by Alex Wolpert and operates from a former glue factory in Bow, close to the Olympic Park. Previously, Wolpert had run the Barworks chain of pubs and bars, and Initial funding for the distillery project came from Wolpert himself and a team of private investors.

A quarter of the total investment was spent on purchasing a bespoke column and pot distilling system from Holstein of Germany, along with a bottling plant that ensures rigorous quality control. "It's lovely to have ownership and autonomy over all the processes," says Wolpert. "A box of gin does not leave the premises if the box or label isn't right – it's checked at every step."

From modest beginnings the business has grown to a level where distillery sales amounted to £1.9m in 2017, while shop takings and income from distillery tours added another £1m to that figure. A recent crowdfunding programme raised around £1.5m, twice the target set by Wolpert and his team, with 80 per cent of that target reached in just one day.

The company is the first gin, vodka and whisky distillery in east London in over 100 years, and started out with four members of staf initially producing some 1,000 bottles of gin for local accounts and also operated a bar at its Bow Wharf site. Staff numbers have swollen to 30, and more than 12,000 bottles per month are now filled under the watchful eyes of Wolpert and head distiller Tom Hills. The Bow Wharf bar at the distillery has been expanded into a restaurant and bottle shop, and a second bottle shop operates in Borough Market.

In addition to its own spirits, the shops sell a range of imported bitters and other spirits, including whiskeys from California's Sonoma County Distilling Company, which produces spirits using direct-fired copper alembic pot distillation. Additionally, East London has collaborated with Wisconsin's Death's Door distillery and Gotlands brewery and distillery in Sweden, as well as using Sonoma whiskey casks for barrel-ageing gin.

According to Alex, the impetus behind the creation of the East London Liquor Company was the fact that "There wasn't anyone on our scale making gin at our price point in the UK. The idea was to make an excellent gin, and not be greedy about the margins, to make a Londoner's gin that everyone can afford."

A London Dry Gin, made from 100 per cent British wheat spirit using vapour and direct infusion, heads the line-up, along with Premium Batch No.1 Gin, flavoured with Darjeeling tea, and Premium Gin Batch No.2 Gin, described as having "a distinctive herbaceous and savoury profile."

The distillery has also ventured into barrel-aged gin, with the first release being a London Dry Gin, that had spent 14 weeks in new French oak casks. Wolpert explains that "The idea is to release a new expression every six to eight weeks, as much for our learning and development as to share this really interesting category with bartenders and customers who are keen to try a slightly different take on gin."

A 100 per cent British Wheat Vodka is distilled in the company's Holstein copper pot still, while perhaps the most unusual product currently available from East London is Demerara Rum. This is produced using molasses from Guyana, and the company describes it as being "microdistilled in a wooden two-column Coffey still – the world's only surviving wooden still – then aged for three years in Bourbon casks."

Wolpert and his team are also enthusiastic about English whisky and are looking forward to the first release of their London Rye later in 2018. According to the distillers, "Each batch we're creating is unique in production, finish and mash bill. Primarily distilling a London Rye, we will be launching various iterations of whisky featuring combinations of pot and column runs and barrel finishes, including new American oak, French oak, chestnut, ex-wine, ex-rye and ex-Bourbon barrels."

Wolpert's ambition is ultimately to release 100,000 bottles of whisky annually, and in relation to the 2018 crowdfunding programme he explains that the company is to expand internationally, focusing on New York, Toronto and China, with the ambitious aim of generating total sales worth £9.6m.

"Our production is at approximately 20 per cent capacity, so we have plenty of room to grow," he says. "Our whisky tastes amazing and we want to produce more of it, quadrupling our production by 2022. We want to expand our sales team to push UK and international growth and get our spirits into more people's glasses."

You must complete form W21 Alcohol duties: Quarterly Distillery Return – declaration of materials used and spirits produced return quarterly for each class of spirit you produce.

We give each distillery a unique five-digit identifying number. We'll notify you of your number and you should use this on your quarterly return.

If you manufacture more than one class of spirits we'll view this as more than one distillery. We'll allocate a unique number for each class of spirits that you produce, for example you'll receive one number for malt spirits and another for grain spirits if you produce both. You must complete your quarterly return (with the correct identifying number) and submit it to the address on the form within 14 days of the end of the calendar quarter.

Returns must be signed by:
- You (as the proprietor)
- A partner or director
- The company secretary.

If this isn't possible, you can allow someone to sign the return on your behalf. This must be in writing:
- In a letter of authorisation to the individual concerned
- Contained in their job description
- Contained in your management control manual
- In some other form contained within your business records."

Chapter Five
Routes to market

---

aking high-quality, authentic spirits with great provenance is all very well, but you won't be making them for very long unless someone buys it!

Distance selling

'Distance selling' – whether by email/website, phone or mail order – can be an invaluable source of income for the microdistiller, establishing a direct connection with individual consumers that may lead to brand loyalty if transactions are fast and friendly. There is also, of course, the added advantage of no 'middleman' to take a percentage, and you know exactly what experience customers have enjoyed because you have been responsible for it.

Inevitably, there is legislation surrounding distance selling, principally intended to protect the public from unscrupulous or inefficient traders, and it pays to know the law before making sales in this way.

It is important to comply with the Consumer Contracts Regulations and the Consumer Rights Act, in addition to which, if you are selling electronically – by email or website – you must also comply with the ecommerce regulations, regardless of whether your customers are individuals or businesses.

According to **www.which.com:**

The Consumer Contracts Regulations 2013

The Consumer Contracts (Information, Cancellation and Additional Charges) Regulations apply to sales of goods or services to consumers without face-to-face contact. This includes selling by mail order, online, using digital television or by telephone, fax or text message. The Regulations replaced the former Distance Selling Regulations.

Under the Regulations, you must:

- Give customers specified information before a sale is made
- Confirm prior and certain other information in a durable form (eg in writing or email)
- Usually give customers a right to cancel their order
- Normally fulfil your contractual obligations within 30 days unless otherwise agreed
- Usually give customers a full refund up to 14 days after receiving their goods, if they change their mind.

Before the sale is made you must supply the following prior or pre-contract information:

- Your business name and, if you require payment in advance, your postal address
- A description of the goods or services and, if you are supplying them on a continuing basis, the minimum term
- The price (including taxes) and how long the price and any special offer will remain valid
- Details of any delivery costs
- How payment can be made
- The arrangements for delivery (or performance of the service);
- Information about cancellation rights
- Whether you will supply a substitute if the goods or services are not available (and, if so, confirmation that you will meet the cost of returning unwanted substitutes)
- If the sale is of digital content, additional information about, for example, its functionality and compatibility.

Durable confirmation

The following information also needs to be provided in writing ('durable' confirmation):

- The prior information (see above)
- How the customer can exercise their cancellation rights, including whether the contract requires them to return unwanted goods if they cancel, and who will pay the costs of returning those goods
- Any guarantees or after-sales service you provide
- Your geographical address for the customer to contact you with any complaints
- For contracts lasting more than one year (or indefinitely), under what conditions the contract can be cancelled.

The confirmation information must be provided in good time – at the latest, when the goods are delivered or the service performed. Information can be provided by letter, fax or email, or in the original mail order advertisement or catalogue.

Cancellation rights

Customers have the right to cancel a purchase within 14 calendar days of receiving goods or the durable confirmation (see above), whichever is later. This 'cooling off' period extends to a maximum of three months and seven working days after delivery if the customer is not given written ('durable') confirmation of the required information, and written confirmation of their right to cancel.

The Consumer Rights Act

The Consumer Rights Act covers goods and services ordered at home (for example through mail order catalogue, direct selling or online) and digital content. All goods must be as described, fit for purpose and of satisfactory quality. If goods are found to be faulty, you must give a full refund up 30 days after the item was purchased. If goods prove faulty up to six months after purchase and they can't be repaired or replaced, consumers are also now entitled to receive a full refund in most cases. Consumers are not entitled to demand a refund or replacement just because they change their mind.

The Ecommerce regulations 2002

The Ecommerce Regulations apply to any sales made electronically: for example, using email, through your website or via text. The regulations apply to sales to businesses as well as to consumers. (Distance sales to consumers using electronic means are covered by both the Ecommerce Regulations and the Consumer Contracts Regulations.

Under the Regulations, when you advertise or sell you must provide information including:

- Your business name, geographical address and contact details;
- Details of trade organisations or professional bodies you belong to
- Information on any authorisation scheme (eg for financial services)
- Your VAT number
- Prices, and whether they include taxes and delivery costs.

Any commercial communications (such as emails) must be clearly identifiable as a commercial communication from you, and clearly identify any promotional offers, competitions or games, and any conditions.

If you have automated systems allowing orders to be placed electronically (eg through your website), you must also provide additional information, including details of how contracts are made and how errors can be corrected. You must also provide prompt confirmation of the order.

Additionally, any advertisements on your website need to

comply with regulations on advertising, and if your website collects information from visitors (for example, using cookies) you must make this clear in a privacy policy. Any personal information collected must comply with data protection rules.

What's allowed

Information included in website adverts and mail shots must adhere to the UK Code of Non-Broadcast Advertising, Sales Promotion and Direct Marketing (CAP code), which essentially requires adverts to be legal, decent, honest and truthful. The CAP code also applies to Facebook, Twitter and any other non-paid-for online space you control (including blogs or other social media sites such as LinkedIn).

Websites and mailshots are also covered by the Consumer Protection from Unfair Trading Regulations. These make it an offence to give false or misleading information about the goods on offer, or to engage in aggressive or misleading selling practices.

If you do not have an existing relationship relating to a similar product, you should not send unsolicited emails, SMS messages or 'spam' to consumers. You must only send messages if the consumer has previously agreed to it, for example by opting in on your website.

Unsolicited marketing calls must not be made to individuals or businesses who have indicated that they do not wish to receive them, either by contract with you or by registering with the Telephone Preference Service. If you are making a marketing call, you must clearly state the name of your business and explain the nature of your call at the start. Similarly, consumers may register with the Mailing Preference Service to state that they do not want to receive direct mail from companies with which they do not have an existing relationship.

Marketing and social media

The principal marketing tools at your disposal are the reputation of your products and the way in which they are presented. Professional sales staff are likely to be beyond the budget of most start-up microdistilling ventures, and there is a degree of satisfaction in achieving sales yourself. After all, nobody has the same degree of commitment and passion to the products in question, more detailed knowledge of how they are made or the type of consumers to whom they are most likely to appeal.

Independent retailers tend to like dealing with actual producers, and the personal touch can often pay dividends. Learn from your mistakes when pitching your spirits and take constructive advice. Most of all, be resilient!

However successful a salesperson you turn out to be, the fact remains that a great deal of your business will be conducted via the internet and by the websites of your company, as well as those of wholesalers and individual retailers.

The more sales you can generate through your own website the better, as you are taking all the profit, and don't have to give a share to a third party. It follows that your website should be well presented, reflecting the ethos of the company and its products, and easy to navigate. Paying for a website designer to work their magic may well turn out to be money well spent.

Social media

When it comes to social media, it is important to feel confident that you are using the medium to its maximum effect and interacting in a credible way with your target demographic. To be effective, social media takes a great deal of nurturing, and you should be aware that it is likely to take up a significant amount of your time. As with website designers, it may pay in the long run to use the services of someone who is really clued in to the likes of Facebook, Instagram and Twitter, though a well written, regularly updated blog on your own website is likely to attract repeat traffic. Make it personal and revelatory where possible – allow readers to feel that they are being taken into the heart of the company and given privileged access to information not otherwise readily available. Bear in mind that this is not a press release.

Media and promotion

Press releases do, however, have an important part to play in announcing new products, events or facilities, and awards won by your spirits. Many microdistillers feel comfortable in creating their own databases of contacts to whom such press releases should be sent, including television and radio media, print and internet journalists, distributors, retailers and existing customers. If composing such press releases, always bear in mind that the person reading it is almost certainly less fascinated by the topic than you are, so keep it tight and factual, include bullet points where possible, give clear contacts for further information and ideally access to imagery.

Other distillers feel that it is worth employing the services of professional PR companies, in order to ensure that the job is carried out with maximum efficiency and professionalism. If choosing to use an agency, decide whether a high-powered London-based company or a lower-key one with more local connections to your area best suits your business model in terms of required levels of exposure, not to mention your budget!

Paid-for advertising is another marketing angle worthy of consideration, but a scattergun approach will be too expensive and not necessarily any more successful than carefully targeted adverts in local newspapers, magazines and specialist drinks publications. As with press releases, keep adverts simple and uncluttered, perhaps employing the services of a graphic designer to make them more eye-catching. Bear in mind that there is no point in advertising unless your products are available for people reading those adverts. Advertise in accordance with your distribution model.

Promotional events at food and drink festivals offer an invaluable way of getting potential purchasers to sample your spirits, and also gives you the chance to engage with them on a one-to-one basis.

If you have a visitor centre at your distillery or offer tours of it on a more modest basis, the same advantages apply as at festivals – the chance to get your spirits into people's mouths and your words into their ears. It is surprising how easily brand loyalty can be encouraged.

If your budget runs to a bespoke visitor centre then there are opportunities to sell not only the whole range of spirits you produce but also branded goods, such as appropriate glasses, t-shirts, baseball caps – the list is practically endless, and such products represent free advertising.

Remember, however, to be true to the brand values you espouse and the connections you wish to make with local heritage and industry. The Three Stills distillery in the Scottish Borders sells a particularly handsome range of tweed caps and scarves, with an original tweed pattern designed and produced by a mill a few hundred yards away. This is appropriate and authentic because the distillery's home town of Hawick has long been a major manufacturer of tweed and knitwear.

Case Study

Ballindalloch
www.ballindallochdistillery.com

Many new distilleries producing whisky follow the same formula of raising money from external investors, offering casks of spirit for sale to the public, releasing new-make spirit to consumers and raising as much revenue as possible through public access to the distillery itself. Not every new distillery conforms to this model, however, and one that certainly doesn't is Ballindalloch, located in the heart of Speyside.

Ballindalloch distillery has been created in a 19th century farmstead by members of the Macpherson-Grant family, who have inhabited nearby Ballindalloch Castle since 1546. Guy Macpherson-Grant, who is the driving force behind the distillery project, is a member of the 23rd generation of his family to live at Ballindalloch Castle, and his great-grandfather, Sir George, was involved with the building of Cragganmore in the 19th century. Indeed, the MacPherson-Grants were co-owners of Cragganmore until 1965.

Ballindalloch has been developed as part of the family estate using existing finances and is being promoted as Scotland's first 'single estate' distillery. All barley used in whisky-making will be grown on the Macpherson-Grants' Home Farm, and the variety currently being cultivated is Concerto.

The first spirit flowed in September 2014 from a plant comprising a one-tonne copper-topped mashtun, four Oregon pine washbacks and a pair of relatively small stills with short necks, to help achieve the desired heavy Speyside style of whisky, in tandem with a pair of worm tubs. The distillery is avowedly manual in operation, with no fewer than 115 hand-operated valves in the system.

'Front of house' at Ballindalloch is Brian Robinson, who for many years was the public face of Glenfiddich in his role as Chief Guide. "Ballindalloch is really just another facet of the sporting and agricultural estate rather than an out and out distilling business," says Robinson. "This is like going back 150 years to what whisky was like then. It's a small, old-style distillery, making a heavy Speyside character of spirit, using worm tubs for condensing purposes rather than modern 'shell and tube' condensers. We're aiming for an old Cragganmore/Mortlach style of whisky, something quite robust, which will make an ideal after-dinner malt, and should suit ex-sherry wood well."

Robinson insists that there is nothing opportunistic about the Ballindalloch distillery venture, noting that "This is not being done on the back of the whisky boom, and no spirit will be released as new-make, or at three years and one day old. We're in no hurry to release it, and we may wait for 8 or 10 years or even longer until it comes onto the market. It will only be sampled while it is young at the distillery 'for discussion,' as it were."

When it comes to welcoming visitors, Ballindalloch takes a very selective approach, with Brian Robinson pointing out that there are a dozen or more distilleries offering excellent 'entry level' tours within a few miles of Ballindalloch, giving them the opportunity to do something different.

"The principal public tour costs £35 per person and lasts for two and a half hours," explains Robinson, "so we are getting people who are serious about their whisky, and the experience we offer them reflects the overall Estate and its values. We also offer an 'Art of Whisky-Making' one-day course, for one or two people only at a time. They turn up at 8.00am and work a full day."

Given the specialist nature of the Ballindalloch visitor experience it comes as no surprise that the visitor centre is the very antithesis of 'corporate,' with the Long Gallery boasting a wood-burning stove, comfortable settees and an array of portraits copied from originals in Ballindalloch Castle, along with furniture and artefacts borrowed from the castle.

Recalling the establishment of the distillery, Robinson notes that "Getting a licence was time consuming. As you might imagine, something like this is complex and you have to ensure that all the i's are dotted and t's are crossed. We had regular contact with an officer in Aberdeen, but the paperwork needed to go to numerous offices to get the necessary sign off.

"From a practical point of view, clearly you need to demonstrate that the buildings are suitable, security is of the requisite high standard and that you can show that you have all the necessary logs and equipment to be able to keep track of what you are making. You don't necessarily need custom software or expensive systems in place, but whatever you use must be able to stand up to any audit. There are also significant financial implications with HMRC requiring, in addition to the licence cost, an up-front payment as a guarantee against future duty liabilities."

He adds that "We received our licence with days to spare before our scheduled start date. If I were to offer any advice to a new applicant it would be to start the process of talking to HMRC much earlier than you think is necessary. As an aside, the licence takes the form of a short letter on one side of A4 paper, it is not the glamorous document you might imagine!"

Robinson is keen to point out that when it comes to ongoing administration, organisation and accuracy are crucial. "From keeping logs of malt and yeast quantities used to the day-to-day detail of noting volumes and gravities, there is something that needs administrative input every day. We fill casks weekly, so we only have to take an account of how much spirit we are filling into casks once a week. We keep notes of how much is filled into each cask, at what strength and where those casks are kept.

"We need to submit returns to HMRC each month detailing our warehousing activity and a quarterly return relating to production. As we have a warehouse that is remote to the distillery, when we move casks there, we also have to issue paperwork for that, too. The key to keeping HMRC happy is to ensure everything is accurate, on time and as I mentioned before, able to be easily audited."

Distribution

No matter how good your product is, all the creative work that has been put into it will come to nothing unless you can get it in front of as many target consumers as possible. Good distribution is arguably more important than any other aspect of running a microdistilling business.

Just who you decide to target depends, to a significant degree, on the scale of production. It may be that local sales through word of mouth and personal contact will create enough sales opportunities to account for everything you can distil. In this case, you can probably carry out your own distribution. All you need is a van.

Usually, however, it is worth looking at specialist outlets beyond your immediate locality. The off-trade may present attractive opportunities by way of specialist wine merchants, farm shops and gift shops, and even country houses and other properties open to the public.

The on-trade, both locally and beyond, also offers great opportunities to get your products in front of consumers. If they buy a measure of your gin, vodka, whisky or sambuca in a pub, hotel bar or restaurant there is a good chance that if they are impressed they will, at some point, buy a bottle.

Both the on-trade and off-trade may give you the chance to host tasting sessions, perhaps in association with other small-scale producers from your locality.

A persuasive way of getting outlets to stock your products is to offer them on consignment; that is leaving a certain number of bottles with the operators without charging them and returning after an agreed period of time to invoice them for the bottles sold. This reduces the financial exposure of the outlet, making them likely to be more amenable to try something new.

If your operation is of sufficient scale, you may wish to sell to national companies that either have multiple outlets or distribute to individual retailers. Such companies would include the likes of Majestic Wines, Adnams plc in East Anglia and Gordon & MacPhail in Elgin, Scotland.

Sales via the internet obviously require hands-on distribution direct from your premises, and a key factor here is to find a reliable, efficient firm of couriers that specialises in handling fragile consignments.

For details of recommended distribution companies see p158.

Rules on labelling and packaging

According to gov.uk, "To sell food and drink products, the label must be:

- Clear and easy to read
- Permanent
- Easy to understand
- Easily visible
- Not misleading

For spirits the label should include the actual alcoholic strength by volume by a figure to no more than one decimal place followed by the symbol '% vol.' and preceded by 'alcohol' or 'alc', the net quantity, name or business name and address of the business operator, country of origin, place of provenance and protected designation of origin if applicable.

Within the EC, "Mandatory information shall appear in a language easily understood by the consumers of the Member States where a [product] is marketed. Within their own territory, the Member States may stipulate that the particulars shall be given in one or more languages from among the official languages of the Union."

Health warnings are not compulsory, but in March 2017 the Department of Health and the British Retail Consortium published new UK labelling guidelines for the alcoholic beverage industry.

The new guidelines follow updated advice from the UK's Chief Medical Officers on the maximum number of units that should be consumed in a week, as well as recommended frequency of alcohol consumption.

The revised label is designed to ensure that shoppers will have access to consistent information and make an informed purchase.

Some 10 months after it appeared, the Royal Society for Public Health (RSPH) declared that all alcoholic labelling should carry mandatory warnings to address what it referred to as an 'awareness vacuum.' The RSPH proposed using traffic light colour coding – such as those on other food items in the UK to indicate levels of fat, salt and sugar – and suggested other information such as the government's 14-unit guideline, the link between alcohol and cancer and drink-driving warnings.

However, John Timothy, chief executive of The Portman Group (the trade group composed of alcoholic beverage producers and brewers), responded by saying that the study showed there was "little public interest in a radical overhaul of drinks labelling" and

86 per cent of respondents to the survey wanted purely factual information and 80 per cent wanted less cluttered labelling."

Christopher Snowden, head of Lifestyle Economics at the Institute of Economic Affairs, backed up Timothy's remarks by declaring that "Mandatory labelling could help to inform consumers if it is strictly factual. Calorie counts, for example, should be carefully considered after Brexit. But the new drinking guidelines have no scientific credibility and companies should not be forced to put suspect information on their products."

Curiously perhaps, there is certain information that spirits' producers might wish to divulge but are prohibited from doing so by EC regulations. Under Regulation 12.3 of the Spirit Drinks Regulation No 110/2008, any mention of a maturation period or age can only refer to the 'youngest alcoholic component' in a spirit.

This causes problems for whisky distillers in particular, who wish to promote 'transparency' in their products. The independent bottler Compass Box had to remove information from two 2016 bottlings, Flaming Heart and This is Not a Luxury Whisky, as the bottler revealed the distilleries involved, the cask types, the ages and the relative proportions in the blend. A complaint led to the Scotch Whisky Association (SWA) informing Compass Box that it had broken the law, and the information in question was subsequently removed from its website.

The website **www.scotchwhisky.com** supported the call for greater transparency, and in January 2017, Bruichladdich CEO Simon Coughlin wrote to the site as follows:

"Bruichladdich were proud pioneers of the No Age Statement (NAS) concept in whisky, but we recognise that our increasingly knowledgeable client base appreciates clear information about the age of every component we use to create our multi-vintage cuvees.

In April 2016 we therefore introduced a 'Classic Laddie Recipe' on our website. Interested clients can simply enter the five digit batch code printed on every bottle of The Classic Laddie to find the particular composition of casks used in each unique vatting.

We are pleased to be able to announce that we have now extended this programme to our heavily peated Port Charlotte Scottish Barley. Exactly the same system applies – there is a field provided on the appropriate product page into which the client can input the batch code and reveal the recipe. Once again, this can be expected to vary from vatting to vatting.

We are confident that, by introducing this greater transparency,

117

Case Study

Dartmoor Distillery
www.dartmoorwhiskydistillery.co.uk

Dartmoor distillery in the Devon town of Bovey Tracey is unusual among English start-ups in that rather than opting to produce white spirits to generate revenue while its whisky matured, only whisky was distilled when the plant became operational in January 2017. A refurbished gin still remains part of future plans.

Local businessman Greg Millar and hotelier Simon Crow were friends and fellow whisky enthusiasts who mused about why nobody had made whisky, at least legally, in the county of Devon, while on a whisky pilgrimage to Islay.

They reasoned that the climate and soil already allowed for the cultivation of high-quality barley, the granite geology of Dartmoor filters renowned spring water and the air quality is excellent, with attendant sea breezes to give optimum maturation conditions. Add to these natural resources many local microbreweries that could supply wash with which to distil, and developing a whisky distillery seemed a matter of common sense!

Millar and Crow were joined in the venture by Andrew Clough, who boasted 40 years' experience in finance, accountancy and business management, and premises were secured in the shape of Bovey Tracey Town Hall, a Grade II listed building dating from 1866.

The team chose to employ the services of a consultant to act as Master Distiller, and the person selected was long-serving former Springbank distillery manager and Director of Production Frank McHardy. He specified the recipe for beer wash which is provided by local brewers, and he chooses the casks in which maturation takes place, with American oak Bourbon barrels, French oak wine barrels, and Spanish sherry barrels currently being filled. According to Simon Crow, "Each barrel gives a different expression to the finished spirit. Some will be bottled from a single barrel type, and some will be bottled according to our Master Distiller's selection of barrels."

When it came to funding the venture, Crow explains that "From the start we were determined to fund without borrowing. It's great having Andrew to support us in managing the financial aspects of our distillery. The financial challenge can be a barrier to starting a whisky distillery. The equipment costs, and three-year wait makes it much harder than starting a gin distillery."

£30,000 was raised via the Kickstarter crowdfunding website, and Crow points out that "It is difficult to be compliant giving away alcohol, and so this is discouraged or prohibited on crowdfunding websites. We offered a variety of different merchandise, visits and events."

He notes that £30,000 was a comparatively modest amount in terms of funding a start-up distillery, explaining that "This was primarily a PR exercise, and a way of learning what interest there may be. We are extremely grateful for the backers' support and encouragement."

One way in which many small-scale whisky distillers raise revenue at an early stage of their business ventures is by the sale of cask 'futures' to individuals or organisations, with these casks being available for bottling once the minimum maturation period of three years has passed. However, this is not part of the Dartmoor team's business plan, and there are also no stated intentions of bottling 'new-make' spirit or 'work in progress' expressions, though Simon Crow does not rule out "...releasing some new spirit in small bottles for visitors to take away."

He adds that "Our first whisky will be released in 2020, and visitor tours are important, as we know whisky enthusiasts like to visit, and they will be our primary customers for our whisky when released, so we are keen to build the tours."

In terms of day-to-day 'housekeeping,' Crow offers an optimistic outlook, declaring that "Once you have navigated the government-issued notices and deciphered them, the ongoing processes are not too onerous. We have processes in place to routinely record and report HMRC returns, and we have received excellent support from our HMRC officer."

When it comes to the actual business of distillation, Dartmoor is equipped with a type of still rarely seen in the UK, namely a French-built former Cognac still. This was acquired from Cognac Master Distiller Miguel D'Anjou who is a member of the third generation distilling Cognac at his farm near Pons in the Cognac region of France. Commissioned by his grandfather in 1966, the 1,400-litres still had been unused since 1994 when the family installed two larger stills.

Explaining the choice of still, Simon Crow says that "Quality distillation equipment is expensive, and often on a long lead time. Greg [Millar] has a strong affiliation to France, and this is how the opportunity presented itself to us. When we researched the potential, we could see that this gave us a way to obtain superb quality equipment.

"The still does not really differ in operation from a 'standard' copper pot. The head is more bulbous than on a traditional whisky still, and this increases the reflux, which contributes to producing a very clean, smooth spirit. The still operates slowly, and this helps, too. The main visual difference is the 'wash warmer' that sits between the still and the condenser. This is mainly for energy recovery, as we pre-heat the second run whilst distilling the first. It also increases the time that the liquid is in contact with copper, which can only be good."

we continue to comply with both the spirit and the letter of the relevant EU legislation (Regulation 12.3 of the Spirit Drinks Regulation No 110/2008), the fundamental purpose of which is to protect the interests of the consumer.

We believe the following quote from the regulation supports our position: "The measures applicable to the spirit drinks sector should contribute to the attainment of a high level of consumer protection, the prevention of deceptive practices and the attainment of market transparency and fair competition. By doing so, the measures should safeguard the reputation which Community spirit drinks have achieved in the Community and on the world market by continuing to take into account the traditional practices used in the production of spirit drinks as well as increased demand for consumer protection and information."

Exporting

There is no doubt that exporting spirits from the UK is big business. According to The Wine & Spirit Trade Association figures, £1.25 billion litres of spirits were exported during 2015, including 1.2 billion bottles of whisky, 204 million bottles of gin and 54 million bottles of vodka. Since 2000, gin exports have risen by 166 per cent in value and 73 per cent in volume.

If planning to export your spirits, take as much advice as you can from other businesses that have already gone down the export route. Another very useful resource is Open To Export **www.opentoexport.com,** a free online information service from The Institute of Export & International Trade, dedicated to helping small UK businesses get ready to export and expand internationally.

One factor working in exporters' favour is that British goods are cheaper to import than they were a year and more ago due to the relatively weak state of the pound at the time of writing. Having established a thriving domestic trade, it is logical to try to replicate that trade in other markets and thereby increase the profitability of your business up to the point where production capacity is reached.

When it comes to exporting, one of the key elements in determining success is the establishment of a viable pricing model. Production costs are at the heart of any pricing model if an acceptable profit margin is to be achieved, and transport costs and any applicable tariffs should also be borne in mind. For example, while India represents a vast market for British spirits of all kinds, a

150 per cent tariff on imported spirits serves to curb the enthusiasm of microdistillers keen to export there.

Additionally, if you are selling to an overseas distributor or major retailer, a significant discount will be expected. As with any pricing policy, be aware of the competition to your own product in the export market in question. Consider not only the obvious opposition, but relatively local or national variants that may not immediately be apparent, but which could well affect the attractiveness of your product.

If you are fortunate, having established a strong reputation for your products in the domestic arena you may be approached by overseas companies keen to import them. It is important for the success of such a venture that the potential importer is a good 'fit' with your business, and nothing beats a one-to-one meeting with key individuals to determine whether the relationship is likely to be mutually beneficial.

The same applies if you are seeking out importers on your own initiative. The ideal importer is one who takes delivery of stock, sells it, deals with direct sales and ecommerce and handles social media. Having established a route to market via an importer or major retailer, it is important to maintain regular contact with them and ensure that social media relating to your product in the country in question is continually nurtured.

It stands to reason that a microdistiller cannot export to every country in the world, due to availability of liquid, apart from the sheer amount of time such an enterprise would take. The word 'micro' implies a clear limit to the amount of spirits being made. It is therefore important to select markets that promise the optimum return, and by 'optimum' we do not necessarily mean the largest profit in the shortest time. Exporting should be seen as a long-haul venture, a marathon rather than a sprint.

France and the USA are the leading markets for Scotch whisky, both in terms of volume and value, and Asia, Taiwan, Japan and South Korea boast many appreciative consumers. Meanwhile, Hong Kong has emerged as a key market for microdistilled gin, due in part to the large British 'ex-pat' community there, and the increasing trend for Chinese drinkers to switch to gin.

Relatively straightforward internet research should give you a good sense of optimum countries to target, and optimum regions or cities within those countries. A city with a dozen dedicated gin bars is probably worth visiting. Similarly, monitoring social media can be an invaluable way of keeping tabs on what drinks are becoming popular and the hotspots where they are being consumed.

There is something of a gin 'season' in the UK, which excludes the winter months, but in Australia, for example, the opposite is true, with January and February marking the start of gin's popularity. Exporting to Australia therefore helps to even out the spirit's sales seasonality.

Exporting may also mean changing packaging, with different or additional labels to provide information – particularly relating to health warnings – that is legally required in some overseas markets, though not in the UK. Additionally, the US works with 75cl bottles rather than the European standard 70cl bottles, and if exporting to hot countries it may be necessary to use screw caps rather than cork stoppers, as the heat inside freight containers can cause the spirit to expand and dislodge the cork.

Above all, value personal interaction and keep close tabs on rules, regulations and requisite paperwork. If you thought there was a lot of bureaucracy involved in setting up your distillery in the first place, then when you come to sell your spirits abroad you can expect even more! The trick is to be thorough and highly organised. That way it shouldn't be too much of a chore, and the rewards will surely be worth the effort.

Tax on spirits and Brexit implications

At the time of writing, the whole issue of exporting is in a state of flux as the UK prepares to leave the EU. At present, as Open To Export explains, "The UK's trading arrangements with countries around the world are shaped by the agreements put in place by the EU. The trading bloc has arranged the UK's trade agreements with partners around the world and of course the UK's trading arrangements with much of Europe have been governed by the rules of being part of the EU.

"When the UK has negotiated its exit from the EU, it will be in a position where it needs to start negotiating deals with partners around the world. This potentially includes the EU, depending on whether the two parties successfully agree a trade agreement as part of the negotiations for leaving.

"The Free-Trade Agreements (FTAs) that the UK goes on to negotiate with new partners could become a major factor for UK businesses when deciding where they could export their goods and services to."

Without an FTA in place, World Trade Organisation rules apply, with a principle of non-discrimination at their heart. This means that no single country can be offered more or less preferential trading terms than any other – tariffs on any one type of goods must be the same for all trading partners.

According to Open to Export, "The reality remains that leaving the EU will make selling goods and services overseas a harder and more time-consuming task with The Institute of Export and International Trade reporting that the number of shipments into and out of the UK to be classed as exports/imports is to rise from 90 million to 300 million per annum. Simply put, while at the moment you can send products to France or Germany without much hassle, once the UK has left the EU there will potentially be a new set of paperwork to complete and obligations to meet in order to continue to sell into these EU markets – and that's before talking about exporting outside of Europe."

One arena in which Brexit may bring good news to the spirits' world is what used to be known as 'duty free' and since 1999 has been labelled 'travel retail.' The change abolished duty free shopping within the EU, but when the UK leaves the European Union on 29 March 2019, it effectively becomes a 'third country'. Under existing EU law, European travellers can make purchases on a duty-free basis if they travel to a 'third country' – i.e. one outside of its 28 member-states. The European Trade Retail Consortium is now seeking confirmation of the return of duty free sales for travellers between the UK and the EU post-Brexit, and it has the strong support of spirits producers who see new opportunities on the horizon, particularly for high-end products.

Appendices

Appendix I HMRC Notice 39

Notice 39: Spirits production in the United Kingdom

It is your responsibility to exercise control over all aspects of your spirit production including the physical security of your premises, plant, vessels etc; the security of spirits produced; accounting for the spirits produced; rendering returns on time; the examination of losses and identifying their cause; the investigation of any irregularity at your premises; and the implementation and monitoring of reasonable and effective measures to prevent any loss of dutiable spirits. You should make sure your production records take these aspects into account. You may be penalised if you fail to comply with the law.

Approvals and licences

Before you start to produce spirits you must obtain a distiller's licence and apply for approval of the plant and process you intend to use. To apply for a licence complete an application form and send it to:

HM Revenue & Customs
National Registration Unit
Portcullis House
21 India St
Glasgow, G2 4PZ.
Tel 0141 555 3489/3586
Fax 0141 555 3506

You should make the application in the name of the person manufacturing the spirits. If you, as manufacturer, are not also the owner of the premises you may obtain a licence in joint names. If you intend to produce spirits at more than one set of premises you must get a licence for each.

The production of spirits by a person who is not licensed is an offence for which there is a penalty. For information on penalties, go to http://www.hmrc.gov.uk/about/new-penalties/faqs.htm. HMRC may refuse to issue a licence or revoke an existing licence where the largest still to be used has a capacity below 18 hectolitres, or when you cease to manufacture spirits.

To apply for approval of plant and process write to the National Registration Unit providing the following details:

- the location of the proposed distillery
- a full description of the manufacturing process
- the number and description of the vessels used in the manufacturing process and use of all plant, and a plan of the premises.

It is advisable not to acquire land or premises or begin any building operations until HMRC approves your plans. Approval may include conditions which will be reviewed from time to time and may be added to or varied. Significant changes to plant (eg the addition or removal of production vessels) must be notified in writing to the National Registration Unit.

As a producer of spirits (distiller) your premises will be a tax warehouse. Under EU legislation, this is a place where exciseable goods can be produced, processed, held, received and dispatched under duty-suspension arrangements. This does not permit you to receive or store duty unpaid alcohol at your distillery. Spirits may only be received and stored in an excise or distiller's warehouse.

Records and Accounts

The following requirements have the force of law under regulation 6 of the Revenue Traders (Account & Records) Regulations 1992.

You must keep records of all your spirit production. This includes information on processes and operations such as fermentations; distillations, including the start and finish of each distillation period and any process or stage of the process in the manufacture of spirits; and deliveries to the warehouse.

Your normal business records should be enough, but HMRC may ask you to modify them if needed. They do not have to be kept in any particular format, but they must be accurate and up-to-date, completed in ink or other permanently legible material, readily accessible to HMRC and kept for at least six years from the date of the last entry. You must not remove any pages from your records, or obliterate any entry without HMRC's prior agreement. You can keep computerised records, but you must inform HMRC in advance. Your system must be capable of producing readable print-outs whenever requested. HMRC will advise you if you need to make any changes to your system.

You must also keep all records and documents relating

to stock; handling; purchases; sales; imports and exports. HMRC may also wish to look at profit and loss and trading statements; management accounts and reports; balance sheets; internal and external auditor's reports and any other business record. Any incidents which affect operations, for example a breakdown of plant, must also be recorded accurately.

Security and construction of premises and plant

You are responsible for the security of the spirit until the duty is paid. HMRC will check your security systems, and you must pay duty on any losses you cannot explain. HMRC recommends the following security measures and checks.

Distillery: perimeter and building security which deters casual entry and shows signs of forced entry; regular security reviews.

Stillroom and warehouse: restricted access and regular checks of vessels and plant; frequent management checks to ensure any lapses in security are put right.

Vessels and plant: measures to ensure that all vessel openings are locked or sealed and that signs of tampering or pilferage do not go unnoticed; technology that controls access to all areas and vessels on the site.

HMRC also expects all plant to be accessible, readily identifiable and with the exception of working stills, capable of being opened as required for inspection; and that all wash backs, feints receivers and spirit receivers should be gauged and calibrated, with calibration tables readily available.

Manufacturing operations

Distillation periods are accounting periods during which you must carry out all your manufacturing of spirits. A period is usually between a week and a month. If you need a longer period you should contact the Excise Helpline, by calling 0300 200 3700. You must specify the start and finish dates of each period in your records. If you manufacture more than one class of spirits (see below) you must specify separate periods for each class of spirit. These periods may run simultaneously. Every distillation period should be clearly identifiable in your business records.

You must complete form W21 Quarterly Distillery Return – Declaration of Materials Used and Spirits Produced, at the end

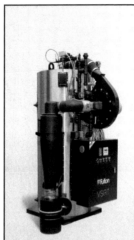

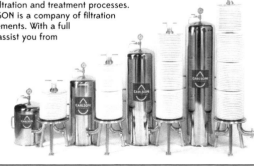

the drinks report

Design   Marketing   Packaging

TheDrinksReport.com is the online magazine for the wine, beer and spirits trade. It features news, views and ideas from the world of drinks with a focus on the marketing and packaging of all alcoholic drinks and is the only global publication dedicated to the packaging and marketing of alcoholic drinks. There are news pages on wine, beer and spirits, drinks packaging design and technology and general business news.

For more information and to sign up
for our weekly newsletter, visit:

www.thedrinksreport.com

of March, June, September, and December. You will need to complete a separate return for each class of spirits you produce. Each distillery has a unique five-digit identifying number. If you manufacture more than one class of spirits you will be allocated a unique number for each class. You may be liable to a penalty if your return is inaccurate and, as a result, you do not pay enough duty or if you do not notify HMRC that a duty assessment is too low. If you know you have made a mistake on your return, you must notify them as soon as possible: they may be able to reduce the penalty. If you deliberately make a false duty return, you may face prosecution for the offence and incur a heavy penalty.

When you manufacture spirits you may use only the processes for which you have received approval, and comply with any conditions HMRC has specified. If you wish to change an existing process or use a new process contact the Excise Helpline, by calling 0300 200 3700.

Duty-unpaid samples of wort, wash, feints and spirits may be taken for the purposes of quality control, strength testing, scientific research, reference, and other production-related analysis. However, you must note the samples taken in your business records, keep the quantity to the minimum necessary, label the samples as 'duty-unpaid sample – not for sale,' destroy samples no longer required and keep records of their use and disposal.

Measuring wort, wash and gravity

You must measure the quantity and gravity of wort and wash collected using recognised industry methods and equipment, in accordance with the manufacturer's protocol, and keep accurate records.

Instruments for measuring alcoholic strength, including automatic densimeters, must comply with regulation 18 of the Spirits Regulations 1991 (as amended). The density must be directly measured as density in air, not density in vacuum converted to density in air, and the temperature of the liquid must be 20°C – the measurement cannot be taken at a different temperature and converted to the equivalent density at 20°C. All of the approved densimeters have been five decimal place machines, and when used according to the instructions have proved to be accurate and precise enough for HMRC. Some machines can convert the density of a liquid to the alcoholic strength from an internal look-up table. Such machines must use the Official HMRC

Laboratory Alcohol Tables to convert the density in air value to an alcoholic strength.

Low wines, feints and spirits

You may remove any fusel oil which has separated from the feints in the feints receiver, or collected in oil traps, but you must measure the quantity and strength of the fusel oil before you dispose of it and record the details in your records. Duty is not charged on fusel oil which is below 8.7 per cent ABV, but no spirits or feints should be mixed with the oil. If it contains more than 8.7 per cent alcohol by volume, it must be 'washed' so that the ABV is reduced to 8.7 per cent or below before it is removed from the distillery. If the strength of any fusel oil is greater than 8.7 per cent, the whole product is liable to duty at the spirits rate.

Normally you will carry feints forward from one manufacturing period to another. If you have feints which you no longer wish to use in the manufacture of spirits, these should be isolated and an account taken of them. They should then be warehoused or destroyed. Your records must show what you have done with the feints. If you destroy or dispose of feints you will need to alter your Whisky Export Refund Scheme claim. You may re-distil low wines and feints at any time. You should ensure that the details of operations to re-distil low wines, feints and spirits are recorded in your business records.

Accounting for and warehousing of spirits
* You must keep a record of the spirits you have produced. The record must include the following details:
* the date and time
* the receiver or other vessel
* the dip or gauge reading
* the temperature and hydrometer readings, and
* the quantity of spirits, adjusted to a temperature of 20°C, with details of bulk volume, strength, and
* litres of alcohol produced.

The spirits should be sent to an approved warehouse immediately after you have entered the details of the spirits account in your business records. If your spirit receiver is also approved as a warehouse vat, they will consider the spirits to be warehoused as soon as the account has been taken and declared in your records. You can find further information about distiller's warehouses in

Notice 197 Excise Goods: Receipt into and Removal from an Excise Warehouse of Excise Goods.

Duty

Excise duty is not normally payable until the spirits are taken out of warehouse (for examples of the excise duty calculation for spirits, see Notice 197), but you may be asked to pay duty on any losses that occur at your distillery or while transferring spirits to a warehouse, which are not due to natural wastage or for which you do not have a valid reason. Duty is normally based on the litres of alcohol contained in the spirits and feints less the litres of alcohol in feints brought forward from the previous period. This is known as the actual charge. The rate of duty on spirits is shown in Part 12, Volume 1, of the integrated Tariff of the United Kingdom which can be found either on **www.hmrc.gov.uk** or by phoning the Excise Helpline, 0300 200 3700.

If the amount of spirits produced is not what you expected you should investigate the reasons why this has happened. Your business records should show the steps you have taken to look into the matter and your findings. If, having completed your investigations, you have found no satisfactory explanation for the loss, then you should provide a written explanation of what has happened. HMRC may assess for duty on the loss.

Appendix II: HMRC Notice 196

Notice 196: Excise goods – authorisation of warehousekeepers and approval of premises

Approvals, authorisations and registrations

Only persons who can demonstrate that they are fit and proper to carry out an excise business will be authorised or registered as excise warehousekeepers. Failure to apply for authorisation or approval at the correct time can attract a financial penalty.

HMRC will visit the authorised excise warehouse-keepers and approved premises of excise goods in duty-suspension to carry out checks on production, operations and warehousing. If you do not provide safe access, HMRC will restrict or withdraw your authorisation.

The warehousekeeper must display prominently the warning poster Notice 50 Duty-free warehouse warning at each entrance and exit to the site. Notice 50 explains that excise goods in the warehouse may be duty-suspended and that improperly removing them may incur severe penalties including imprisonment.

HMRC will normally arrange appointments to visit but may also make unannounced visits. You must permit HMRC officers access to any area of the warehouse during operating hours or at any time when activity is taking place at the warehouse.

Applying for authorisation

To apply for authorised excise warehousekeeper status, complete Form EX61 Excise Warehousekeeper – Application for Registration, which is available from the HMRC website. If you are a partnership you must also complete form EXCISE 102.

The application form must be completed and signed by the sole proprietor, one of the partners if the business, or a director or the company secretary or an authorised signatory. Completed forms should be returned to the National Registration Unit (NRU).

You must apply at least 45 working days before the date on which you wish your authorisation to begin to allow HMRC time to carry out the necessary verification and pre-approval checks, which will include a visit. Your application will be vetted and is subject to background checks. Should these checks provide insufficient assurance that the business is suitable for authorisation, further information may be requested. Until this information is received, your application will be put on hold.

During the visit HMRC will examine all the business's activities and may enquire about its suppliers, customers, business plans, accounting systems, premises, financial viability and so on. Only when it is satisfied the business is a genuine enterprise which is commercially viable, with a genuine need for authorisation and that all key persons are fit and proper to carry on such a business will it process the application.

Reasons for refusing an application may include circumstances where:

- The legal entity (this includes the directors and key employees) has been involved in revenue non-compliance or fraud.
- The application is incomplete or inaccurate.
- You (the directors in the case of a limited company) have unspent convictions.
- There are proven links between the legal entity orkey employees with other known non-compliant or fraudulent businesses.
- The business is not commercially viable.
- You have not been able to demonstrate the business is genuine.
- You have outstanding HMRC debts
- The legal entity has been involved in significant revenue non-compliance.
- You are unable to provide adequate financial security.
- You do not have a satisfactory accounting system.
- If HMRC is not satisfied with the information provided to us, it may refuse to authorise you. If you fail to provide the information requested, it will place your application on hold until it is received. It will notify you of the reason or reasons for refusal.

Record keeping

Record-keeping requirements are laid down in Notice 206 Revenue traders records. All records must be permanent and legible and must show details of all excise goods received, stored in and removed from the warehouse. Your stock accounts must show:

- A full description of the goods (including age and date of first warehousing for spirits).
- The current location of goods in the warehouse.

- The duty status of the goods, and evidence of any duties paid.
- The name, address and, if appropriate, the VAT Registration Number of the owner, and, if applicable, the duty representative.
- Whether the goods have been subject to a supply in warehouse, and
- A means of identifying all goods to their stock number or vice versa.

If you wish to use computers for stock control and/or accounting purposes you should include this request in your application for approval, providing full details of the system you intend to adopt. The standard of records stored on your computer must be equivalent to that required if you were to use manual records.

When considering granting approval to use your specified software package HMRC requires:

- Right of access to your computer systems and to data and documentation including financial and management systems.
- The facility to download data for checks and audit work off-site.
- Any necessary assistance in carrying out audits of your systems.
- Adequate back-up and disaster recovery systems.
- A terminal for official use capable only of printing, reading files, and displaying information on the VDU.
- A unique password to allow officers access to files on a read-only basis.

Stock marking and control

You must mark all excise goods so that you can identify them in your stock accounts. Excise goods must have clear and tamper-proof markings at all times from arrival at to removal from duty-suspension. You may use any system which meets this requirement (for example, bar coding), providing that you can establish an audit trail.

Your stock account must show:

- a commercial description of the product
- the quantity received in litres of alcohol
- the alcoholic strength of the product

- the quantity received in cases, casks and/or polydrums
- a unique identifying reference number
- the date received
- the owner of the goods.

You should keep all excise goods in clearly identified locations so that you can readily trace them to the stock account. You must note the appropriate stock account whenever you move excise goods to a new location in the warehouse. You must check the accuracy of your stock by undertaking a satisfactory inventory-checking system as agreed with HMRC and by complete stocktaking at reasonable intervals. You must take stock of all excise goods in the excise warehouse monthly in the case of bulk goods in vats or in storage tanks or annually in the case of all other excise goods. HMRC may ask you to produce all stocktaking records and working papers and carry out a stocktake if there is reasonable cause.

As authorised warehousekeeper, you are responsible for control of the goods in your approved sites. You must take all necessary steps to control and safeguard your stocks and investigate and examine critically all losses and deficiencies.

You must record all the losses and the results of your investigations into them, including any management decisions taken, take prompt remedial action, report losses or deficiencies to HMRC and note the loss in the stock account.

Failure to report notifiable losses immediately is a serious breach of your conditions of approval, and could lead to its revocation. HMRC will charge duty on losses and deficiencies unless you can show they are due to natural causes or accident. Your records must contain a clear audit trail to justify any adjustments of stock records following the discovery of any errors. If at any time you discover a discrepancy in your stock you must immediately contact the Excise and Customs Helpline on 0300 200 3700.

General storage and distribution warehouses

To apply for General Storage and Distribution Warehouse ('bonded warehouse') approval, use form EX68. To gain approval you should have a minimum potential duty liability of £500,000 on the average monthly stockholding of duty-suspended goods, or a duty liability of at least £2,000,000 on an annual throughput.

Trade facility warehouses

A trade facility warehouse is approved for a specific purpose that has to be completed within duty suspension; for example, a bottling operation. Approval will stipulate the period that duty-suspended goods may be stored on the premises before and after the approved activity takes place. Once the purpose of the trade facilitation has been completed, the goods must either be duty-paid, removed to a warehouse approved to store such goods or exported. Complete form EX69 to apply.

Financial guarantees

An approved guarantor (for example, a financial institution) must undertake to pay HMRC in the event of a chargeable loss where the person liable fails to pay. Authorised warehousekeepers should contact the Financial Securities Centre (FSC) for further details about applying for a premises guarantee. Guarantees are the only form of security acceptable to HMRC. Only companies approved by HMRC may act as guarantors. Most banks and insurance companies have this approval. The cost of maintaining the guarantee is a commercial arrangement between you and the guarantor.

Potential duy on month-end stock holding	Level of Security
<£100,000	Nil
>£100,000 but <£400,000	£100,000
>£400,000 but <£1m	25 per cent of potential duty
>£1m but <£25m	£250,000
>£25m but <£100m	1 per cent of potential dury
>£100m	£1m

Your liability is not restricted to the size of the guarantee. HMRC can assess the liability for outstanding duty arising from any chargeable loss in the warehouse which may be significantly greater than the size of the guarantee.

For general storage and distribution warehouses HMRC will base the level of security on the potential duty due on average end-of-month stock calculated over a 12-month period, allowing for any seasonal variations. For trade facility warehouses it bases its calculation on the proposed or current throughput levels.

The minimum level of security for new general storage and distribution warehouses is £250,000.

HMRC will offer a reduction of the guarantee levels for established traders if it has made no claim against the security and no significant irregularities have been identified.

Where the principal qualifies for a reduction in the level of security and the new security required would be less than £100,000, no security is required.

As an authorised warehousekeeper you must inform the FSC if your trading pattern changes, as it could result in an increased or reduced level of guarantee.

In the following circumstances its may allow reductions for premises security as follows:

If the principal has	And HMRC has	The level of security is reduced
Provided security for the two previous consecutive years.	Made no claim against the security and no significant irregularities have been identified.	By 50 per cent
Provided security for the previous four consecutive years.	Made no claim against the security and no significant irregularities have been identified.	No guarantee is required.

Approval to carry out operations in warehouse

The only allowable operations in distillers' warehouses are:
- bottling of spirits produced at the associated distillery
- reducing spirits with water
- filling casks or drums with spirits
- removing spirits in bulk by tanker or authorised pipeline
- drawing off spirits from unsound casks or pumping direct from casks to tanker
- emptying casks into vats for removal in bulk
- transferring spirits from cask to cask
- If you wish to carry out an operation that is not listed above or are in any doubt that your action is allowable, contact the Helpline on 0300 200 3700, giving full details of the proposed operation

When carrying out any operation on duty-suspended goods, you must take accurate records immediately before and after each operation, keep an accurate record of any cleaning agent used, and advise HMRC about any gains and losses from any operation in the warehouse.

For each bottling operation you must:
- take account prior to bottling
- take and record bottle measurements of strength and liquid content
- carry out filling adjustments to make sure that the intended strength and quantity are achieved in practice
- allocate an identifying stock number to filled cases
- investigate any losses outside established loss patterns
- investigate all gains during the operation
- complete a declaration of outturn – if more than one size of bottle is to be filled, record the number of cases of each size
- secure any remnant
- complete your stock accounts
- keep a copy of the bottle label used
- keep a record if you use duty-free spirit for rinsing.

Determining strength and volume

In order that the strength and volume of product may be determined for duty and stock control purposes, you must have a system in place that meets the requirements of Section 2 of ALDA, Regulation 31 of the Excise Warehousing (etc.) Regulations 1988 (EWER), and Regulations 18 and 19 of the Spirits Regulations 1991.

You may use any recognised method to determine alcoholic strength provided that the results are accurate and the method is used consistently. The method used to settle any dispute will depend on the type of product, for example, for spirit the method used will be the hydrometer referred to in the Spirit Regulations.

You must record alcoholic strength and volume as accurately as possible, ensuring that you adjust for any obscuration caused by the presence of sweetening, colouring or other ingredients. During an operation to bottle duty-suspended product in the warehouse, you must give prior notice of the intended strength and quantity per case (for example 12 × 40 per cent × 70cl = 3.36 litres of alcohol). You should take and record sufficient measurements during each operation of the liquid content and strength. You must keep a sample of each bottle label used and any other document which specifies the quantity and strength of the goods. You must be able to demonstrate that when measuring strength and volume you make a continuing genuine effort to achieve the strength and volume indicated on bottles or other containers.

HMRC will normally accept the labelled strength and volume as the basis of duty calculations if you can show that you are not aiming to achieve a higher strength than that shown on the label and that, if the actual strength exceeds the label strength, you take corrective action immediately. It may ask you to pay additional duty if it finds that you have packaged goods at strengths or volumes exceeding those on the labels.

Excise warehouse returns (form W1)

All warehousekeepers with the exception of certain trade facility warehouses are required to submit a W1 stock return which shows stock movements and stock on hand at the end of the return period, normally on a monthly basis. Returns must be received within 14 days of the end of each return period. If you fail to submit a W1 return on time this may result in a financial penalty. If you persistently fail to submit returns it could result in the withdrawal of your authorisation.

Appendix III: Notice 197

Notice 197: Excise Goods: receipt into and removal from an excise warehouse of excise goods

General information

You may remove goods from an excise warehouse for:

- home use on payment of duty (sometimes referred to as 'released for consumption').
- dispatch under duty suspension to other approved UK warehouses, including those on the Isle of Man.
- dispatch under duty suspension to approved persons or premises in other EU Member States.
- export to non-EU countries in duty suspension.
- entitled miscellaneous removals.
- This list is not exhaustive. You should contact HMRC before removing goods from the warehouse for any other purpose unless we make a specific reference to that purpose in this notice or in your approval. **You must observe certain rules before removal**:
- unless HMRC has agreed otherwise, take account of the goods to be removed and carry out any necessary examination.
- write the goods out of your stock account.
- ensure that duty is paid or accounted for on removals for home use.
- make sure that you supervise and check the removal is accurate before the goods leave the warehouse.
- In your own interests you should carry out sufficient checks to confirm that all your customers are genuine traders who are aware of their responsibilities in respect of excise goods.

You must individually record all removals for stock return purposes and keep a schedule of different types of removals. If HMRC has restricted your approval to specific types of removals (for example, repacking operations and returning the goods to the original supplying warehouse), you may ask to remove goods for a different purpose, such as exports, by asking for a variation to your approval. The procedure for obtaining a variation is detailed in Notice 196. If you remove goods for purposes other than those in your approval, HMRC may revoke your approval.

All warehouses approved to store UK-produced whisky

or whiskey must complete annual return Form W1A. The warehousekeeper, must provide details of the stock in warehouse at 31 December each year and information of movements made during the preceding year. HMRC will issue this form together with completion instructions.

Removal to home use by duty payment

You can only remove excise goods from your warehouse on payment of duty and within the conditions set out in your approval. You must take all necessary steps to pay the duty accurately and by the due dates. Failure to do so may result in prosecution or a financial penalty and could lead to restriction or withdrawal of your warehouse-keeper authorisation.

The systems, procedures and records to be kept and prepared when removing excise goods to home use will have been agreed at the time your approval and authorisation was granted. You must follow these procedures without exception. Before you remove goods to home use you must use the appropriate payment warrant documentation. This may be completed manually or online using either an online warrant or HMRC's XML service.

When payment is made by cash or equivalent, use warrants W5 for the removal of alcohol goods. When you are approved to defer payment of duty and wish to account for the duty using the deferment process, use warrant W5D. Paper warrants should be sent by post to the National Warrant Processing Unit (NWPU). Each warrant must contain a Consecutive Reference Number (CRN). HMRC strongly advises that you do not remove any goods until you are certain your warrant has been accepted. Copies of all forms and the notes to assist completion are available on the HMRC website.

HMRC also has a facility for the submission of remittance warrants and duty deferment warrants online, ATWD, available on the HMRC website. The online declaration service pre-populates standing data, including warehouse details, making it easier to complete the form and automatically calculates the amount of duty due as well as sub-totals, the amount of VAT, and the grand total. It also provides an immediate on-screen acknowledgement of receipt, confirms the approval of deferment warrants within a few minutes rather than having to wait for HMRC to reply by post, and provides a 24-hour service. To use the ATWD online service you will need to register and enrol for the service via the Government Gateway website.

The XML Direct Submission Service allows you to send data directly from your computer to HMRC. This allows you to submit large numbers of warrants directly from your duty management systems via XML, rather than re-keying the warrants on to an online screen. The XML format for exchanging information between computer systems is a stable and widely adopted technology but does not allow HMRC to access or interrogate your computer system, only to receive information, confirm receipt and pass back messages about invalid entries or format errors.

If you are not approved to use deferment arrangements, before removing goods from your warehouse you must complete cash remittance advice W5 and submit it to the NWPU together with your remittance. Remittances may take the form of cash; a banker's draft; a cheque covered by banker's standard guarantee (form C&E 307); a cheque individually guaranteed by the bank, endorsed 'guaranteed' or 'good', countersigned by the bank manager or other responsible official; BACS (for sums less than £20,000,000) or CHAPS. If you wish to pay by electronic transfer then you should contact the NWPU.

Deferment of duty

To apply to defer daily payment of excise duty and make monthly direct debit payments, follow the guidance set out in Notice 101 Deferring Duty, VAT and Other Charges. Before your application is approved, you must take out a guarantee to cover your total monthly liabilities for the particular category of duty or VAT concerned. If you repeatedly exceed your guarantee level or deferment limit, your duty deferment facility will be suspended and may be withdrawn. If this happens you will be asked to make immediate cash payment and you will not be able to remove any goods until your payment has been received by the NWPU. You can provide supplementary guarantees to cover liabilities in periods of greater trade.

For all removals from your warehouse under deferred duty arrangements, you must make sure that the NWPU receives completed W5D and W6D forms for all that day's removals no later than the end of the following working day, unless HMRC has agreed scheduling arrangements. HMRC will confirm receipt by returning a stamped copy of the form, but the return of the copy only means that HMRC has received the form. In your own interests you may wish to delay removing the goods from your warehouse until you are sure that your deferment account has been debited.

Denaturing (contaminating) and destroying alcohol

If any distillate held in duty suspension is surplus after operations, of less value than the duty liable on it, or in an unmarketable condition, you may apply to HMRC for permission to denature (ie contaminate to make unpotable, usually with methanol) or destroy it without having to pay the duty. If someone else carries out the denaturing or destruction on your behalf, you remain responsible for ensuring that you comply with all HMRC procedures. You must give at least two working days' notice if you wish to carry out the procedure on your premises or five working days' notice if the procedure is to be conducted elsewhere.

You must inform HMRC why you wish to denature or destroy the goods, the description and quantity of the goods concerned, the potential amount of duty involved, the date, time and place of the proposed procedure, the proposed method and the purpose to which denatured product will be put. Notifications should be sent by email to niualcohol@hmrc.gsi.gov.uk or by fax to 0141 555 3545. If HMRC decides that your proposed method of denaturing is not satisfactory it will tell you in writing. You are required to provide evidence that the goods have been denatured or destroyed in accordance with the notice given. Any discrepancies will be treated as a loss in warehouse.

Duty-paid goods may also be denatured or destroyed. To claim duty drawback, follow the directions set out in Notice 207.

Calculation of excise duty

Unless HMRC has permitted the use of an alternative method that does not disadvantage the revenue, you must work out each constituent stage of the calculation process to a minimum of four decimal places. But to complete the remittance advice W5 or W5D, truncate the quantity of alcohol established at the end of the calculation process to two decimal places.

Please see the following examples.

(a) 800 cases of vodka, each containing 6x70cl @ 37.5% ABV 6 x 0.7 x 37.5 per cent = 1.575LPA x 800 = 1,260 x duty @ £28.74= £36,212.40

(b) 79 cases of whisky, each containing 12 x 70 cl x 43% ABV 12 x 0.7 x 43 per cent = 3.612LPA x 79 = 285.348LPA total x £28.74 = £8,200.90.

(c) 1,209 cases of gin, each containing 12 x 1 litre x 40% ABV 12 x 1 x 40 per cent = 4.8 LPA x 1209 = 5803.2 LPA x £28.74 = £166,783.96

Appendix IV: Reviews and Appeals

Reviews and appeals, stautes, HMRC contacts

Review and appeal procedures

When HMRC makes a decision you can appeal against, it will inform you and offer a review. It will explain the decision and tell you what you need to do if you disagree. Examples include the amount of an assessment, the issue of a civil penalty or a decision specifically connected to the relevant duty. You will usually have three options. Within 30 days you can send new information or arguments to the officer you have been dealing with, have your case reviewed by a different officer or have your case heard by an independent tribunal. A review will be handled by a different officer from the one who made the decision. If you prefer to have an independent tribunal hear your case, you must write directly to the Tribunals Service.

If you want HMRC to review a decision, you must write to the officer who issued the decision letter within 30 days of the date of the letter. HMRC will complete its review within 45 days unless it agrees another time-limit with you. If you have asked for a review you cannot ask the tribunal to hear your case until the 45 days (or the time-limit you agreed) has expired, or HMRC told you the outcome of its review. If you are not satisfied with the review's conclusion, you have 30 days to ask the tribunal to hear your case.

If you do not want a review you may appeal to the independent tribunal. You need to send your appeal to the Tribunals Service within 30 days of the date on the decision letter.

You can find further information about reviews and appeals in factsheet HMRC1 HMRC Decisions – 'What to do if you disagree'. You can download it from HMRC's website, or call the Revenue & Customs Orderline on 0300 200 3610. You can also find more information about how to appeal on the Tribunals Service website or by phoning 0845 223 8080.

The Law

You will find the main primary, secondary, and European legal provisions governing the contents of HMRC Notices in:

- The Alcoholic Liquor Duties Act 1979 (ALDA)
- The Customs and Excise Management Act 1979 (CEMA)

- The Denatured Alcohol Regulations 2005 (SI 2005/1524)
- The Excise Duties (Deferred Payment) Regulations 1992 (SI 1992/3152)
- The Excise Goods (Drawback) Regulations 1995 (SI 1995/1046)
- The Excise Goods (Holding, Movement and Duty Point) Regulations 2010 (SI 2010/593)
- The Excise Warehousing (etc.) Regulations 1988 (SI 1988/809)
- The Revenue Traders (Accounts and Records) Regulations 1992 (SI 1992/3150)
- The Spirits (Rectifying, Compounding and Drawback) Regulations 1988 (SI 1988/1760)
- The Spirits Regulations 1991 (SI 1991/2564)
- The Warehousekeepers and Owners of Warehoused Goods Regulations 1999 (SI 1999/1278)
- European Council Directive 2008/118/EC OJ: L9, 14.01.09.

Contacting HMRC

In most cases you should be able to find the information you need on the HMRC website, **www.hmrc.gov.uk**. If you cannot find the answer there, your first point of contact should be the Excise Helpline on 0300 200 3700.

If you have a problem with the EMCS registration and enrolment process, contact the EMCS Online Services Helpdesk on 0300 200 3701.

Contact details for other teams or offices mentioned in this Notice are:

HMRC National Registration Unit (NRU)
Portcullis House, 21 India Street,
Glasgow, G2 4PZ,
Phone: 0141 555 3601
Fax: 0141 555 3506

HMRC National Warrant Processing Unit (NWPU)/National Warehouse Return Centre (NWRC)
2nd Floor Portcullis House,
13-21 India Street,
Glasgow, G2 4PZ
Phone: 0141 555 3665
Fax: 0141 555 3555

HMRC National Verification Centre (NVC)
Portcullis House, 21 India Street,
Glasgow, G2 4PZ
Phone: 0141 555 3616

HMRC Financial Securities Centre (FSC)
Portcullis House, 21 India Street,
Glasgow, G2 4PZ
Phone: 0141 555 3505
Fax: 0141 555 3506

Directory of services & suppliers

Please note: The following list is as complete as we could make it but not exhaustive, and we apologise to any providers of supplies and services that have been missed out. Many of the firms listed offer services and supplies in more than one category, but space prevents us from listing each company more than once. It is therefore always worth a thorough check of their websites to see just how wide and varied their activities are. If you would like to be listed in the next edition please email **info@paragraph.co.uk**

ASSOCIATIONS, CLUBS & SOCIETIES

International Centre for Brewing and Distilling
Heriot-Watt University, Riccarton,
Edinburgh, Midlothian,
Scotland, EH14 4AS
+44 (0) 131 451 3183
www.icbd.hw.ac.uk

Scotch Whisky Association
Quartermile Two, 2 Lister Square,
Edinburgh, Midlothian,
Scotland, EH3 9GL
+44 (0) 131 222 9200
www.scotch-whisky.org.uk

BOTTLES & BOTTLING

Ardagh Group
Headlands Lane,
Knottingley, West Yorkshire,
England, WF11 0HP
+44 (0) 1977 674 111
www.ardaghgroup.com

Bottle Company (South) Ltd
Unit 3, Pixash Business Centre,
Pixash lane, Keynsham, Bristol,
England, BS31 1TP
+44 (0) 117 986 9667
www.bottlecompanysouth.co.uk

Broxburn Bottlers
East Mains Industrial Estate,
Broxburn, West Lothian,
Scotland, EH52 5NN
+44 (0) 1506 854 373
www.broxburnbottlers.co.uk

Encirc Group
Ash Road, Elton, Cheshire,
England, CH2 4LF
+44 (0) 1928 725 300
ww.encirc360.com

H & A Prestige Bottling Ltd
Ackhurst Business Park,
Ackhurst Road, Chorley,
Lancashire, England, PR7 1NH
+44 (0) 1257 479 100
www.hacontractbottling.co.uk

Neville and More
Unit 15, Oakhurst Business Park,
Wilberforce Way, Horsham,
West Sussex, England, RH13 9RT
+44 (0) 1403 732 290
www.nevilleandmore.com

Oakbank Products Ltd
6 Fairbairn Road, Livingston,
Scotland, EH54 6TS
+44 (0) 1506 412 937
www.oakbankproducts.com

Rawlings & Son
Unit 3 Crown Road, Warmley,
England, BS30 8JJ
+44 (0) 1179 604 141
www.rawlingsbristol.co.uk

Vetreria Etrusca Ltd.
16 Beckside, Plumpton, Penrith,
Cumbria, England, CA11 9PD
+44 (0) 1768 894 044
www.vetreriaetrusca.it

Wade Ceramics Ltd
Bessemer Drive, Stoke On Trent,
Staffordshire, England, ST1 5GR
+44 (0) 845 481 0206
www.wade.co.uk

BOTTLING MACHINES & SUNDRIES

**Advanced Bottling
UK Ltd (ABUK)**
Brealey Works, Station Street,
Misterton, Nottinghamshire,
England, DN10 4DD
+44 (0) 1427 890 099
www.abuk.co.uk

Carlson Filtration
The Butts Mill, Barnoldswick,
Lancashire, England, BB18 5HP
+44 (0) 1282 811 000
www.carlson.co.uk

Enterprise Tondelli
Unit 7 College Farm Buildings,
Barton Road, Pulloxhill,
Bedfordshire, England, MK45 5HP
+44 (0) 1525 718 288
www.enterprisetondelli.com

Foodmek
17 Shanwell Road South, Tayport,
Fife, Scotland, DD6 9EA
+44 (0) 1382 553 577
www.foodmek.co.uk

Intercaps Filling Systems Ltd
264 Banbury Road, Oxford,
England, OX2 7DY
+44 (0) 1865 520 083
www.icfillingsystems.com

Klockner Pentaplast Group
PO Box 11 65, Montabaur,
Germany, WF11 0BL
+49 2602 915 0
www.kpfilms.com

Krones UK Ltd.
Westregen House, Great Bank
Road, Wingates Industrial Park,
Bolton, Lancashire,
England, BL5 3XB
+44 (0) 1942 845 000
www.krones.co.uk

CASKS & COOPERAGE

Camlachie Cooperage Ltd
Unit R, Clyde Workshops,
Fullarton Road, Glasgow,
Aberdeenshire,
Scotland, G32 8YL
+44 (0) 141 641 9284
www.camlachiecooperage.com

CypherCo Ltd
Unit 19 Rural Enterprise Centre,
Vincent Carey Road,
Rotherwas Industrial Estate,
Hereford, Herefordshire,
England, HR2 6FE
+44 (0) 1432 343 340
www.cypherco.com

Joseph Brown Vats of Dufftown Ltd
33 Balvenie Street, Dufftown,
Scotland, AB55 4AS
+44 (0) 1340 820 265
www.woodenvats.com

Kammac plc
Gladden Place, West Gillibrands
Industrial Estate, Skelmersdale,
Lancashire, England, WN8 9SY
+44 (0) 1695 727 272
www.kammac.com

Mckenzie Pentland
Old Pentland Saw Mill,
Edinburgh, Midlothian,
Scotland, EH20 9NU
+44 (0) 131 440 0301
www.mckenzieskiphire.com

Roe Head Mills
Far Common Road, Mirfield,
West Yorkshire, England,
WF14 0DG
+44 (0) 1924 496 671
www.eurobung.co.uk

Rotech (Swindon) Ltd
10-11 Blackworth Industrial Park,
Highworth, Swindon, Wiltshire,
England, SN6 7NA
+44 (0) 1793 764 700
www.rotechkeg.co.uk

Speyside Cooperage
Dufftown Road, Craigellachie,
Aberlour, Banffshire,
Scotland, AB38 9RS
+44 (0) 1340 871 108
www.speysidecooperage.co.uk

CLOSURES & CORK

C Olley & Sons Ltd
36 Southgate Avenue, Mildenhall,
Suffolk, England, IP28 7AT
+44 (0) 1638 712 076
www.olleycork.co.uk

Erben Packaging & Machinery
Lady Lane, Hadleigh, Ipswich,
Suffolk, England, IP7 6AS
+44 (0) 1473 823 011
www.erben.co.uk

Herti UK Ltd
Astra House, The Common,
Cranleigh, Surrey, England, GU6 8RZ
+44 (0) 1483 266 617
www.herti.co.uk

Macbey Industrial Ltd
Tandem Industrial Estate,
Waterloo, Huddersfield,
West Yorkshire, England, HD5 0BL
+44 (0) 1484 533 216
www.metal-closures.co.uk

Rankin Brothers & Sons
3c Drakes Farm, Drakes Drive,
Long Crendon, Buckinghamshire,
England, HP18 9BA
+44 (0) 1844 203 100
www.rankincork.co.uk

United Closures & Plastics Ltd
1 Steuart Road, Bridge of Allan,
Stirling, Stirlingshire,
Scotland, FK9 4JG
+44 (0) 1786 833 613
www.ucpLtd.com

United Closures & Plastics Ltd
1 Steuart Road, Bridge of Allan,
Stirling, England, FK9 4JG
+44 (0) 1786 833 613
www.gcs.com

Viscose Closures Ltd
Ferryboat Cloase, Swansea
Enterprise Park, Swansea, Wales,
SA6 8QN
+44 (0) 1792 796393
www.viscose.co.uk

COMPUTER SERVICES

**Distillery Records &
Management System (DRAMS)**
40 Carden Place, Aberdeen,
Scotland, AB10 1UP
+44 (0) 1224 627 600
www.drams-software.com

Epicor
No. 1 The Arena, Downshire Way,
Bracknell, England, RG12 1PU
+44 (0) 1344 468 468
www.epicor.com

Merlin Business Software
Chatsworth House, Millennium
Way, Chesterfield, Derbyshire,
England, S41 8ND
+44 (0) 1246 457 150
www.chatsworth.co.uk

The Trapeze Group
The Mill, Staverton, Trowbridge,
Wiltshire, England, BA14 6PH
+44 (0) 808 281 1039
www.trapezegroup.co.uk

Vintner Computer Systems
16 Station Road, Chesham,
Buckinghamshire, England,
HP5 1DH
+44 (0) 1494 792 539
www.vintner.co.uk

DISPENSE SYSTEMS

Anton Paar
13 Harforde Court, John Tate
Road, Hertford, Hertfordshire,
England, SG13 7NW
+44 (0) 1992 514 730
www.anton-paar.com

England Worthside Ltd
Hope Mills, Hope Place,
Keighley, West Yorkshire,
England, BD21 5LJ
+44 (0) 1535 682 222
www.worthside.co.uk

Eurocave Professional
57 Chiltern Street, London,
Greater London,
England, W1U 6ND
+44 (0) 2079 354 679
www.eurocave.co.uk

Hach
Laser House, Ground Floor, Suite
B, Waterfront Quay,
Salford Quays, Manchester,
England, M50 3XW
+44 (0) 1618 721 487
uk.hach.com

Russell Finex Ltd
Russell House, Browells Lane,
Feltham , Middlsex,
England, TW13 7EW
+44 (0) 2088 182 000
www.russellfixen.com

ENGINEERING SERVICES

Abbott & Co (Newark) Ltd
Newark Boiler works,
Newark, Nottinghamshire,
England, NG24 2EJ
+44 (0) 1636 704 208
www.air-receivers.co.uk

ABM Ltd
Pitt Street, Widnes, Cheshire,
England, WA8 0TG
+44 (0) 151 420 2829
www.abm.ltd.uk

Alfa Laval Ltd
7 Doman Road, Camberley,
Surrey, England, GU15 3DN
+44 (0) 1276 633 833
www.alfalaval.co.uk

Bedford Stainless Ltd
5 Faraday Close, Snape Lane
Industrial Estate, Harworth,
Doncaster, South Yorkshire,
England, DN11 8RU
+44 (0) 1302 752 010
www.bedfordstainless.co.uk

Beverage Process Ltd
3 Stable Courtyard, Westhill,
Ledbury, England, HR8 1JF
+44 (0) 1531 631 948
www.beverageprocess.com

Blyth + Blyth
Third Floor, 169 Elderslie Street,
Glasgow, Glasgow,
Scotland, G3 7JR
+44 (0) 141 566 2000
www.blythandblyth.co.uk

Briggs
Richard Sizer, Briggs House,
Derby Street, Burton-upon-Trent,
Staffordshire, England, DE14 2LH
+44 (0) 1283 566 661
www.briggsplc.co.uk

Carbonation Techniques Ltd
Unit E4, Halesfield 5, Telford,
England, TF7 4QJ
+44 (0) 1952 583 901
www.carbotech.co.uk

Clark & Sutherland
Unit 3A Westerton Road North,
Keith, Moray, Scotland, AB55 5FL
+44 (0) 1542 880 100
www.clarkandsutherland.co.uk

Endress+Hauser Ltd
Floats Road, Manchester,
Greater Manchester,
England, M23 9NF
+44 (0) 161 286 5000
www.uk.endress.com

GEA Process Engineering Ltd
Leacroft House, Leacroft Road,
Birchwood, Warrington, Cheshire,
England, WA3 6JF
+44 (0) 1925 812 650
www.geaprocess.co.uk

Gilbert Gilkes & Gordon Ltd.
Canal Head North, Kendal,
Cumbria, England, LA9 7BZ
+44 (0) 1539 720 028
www.gilkes.com

Green Engineering
35 Beaufort Place,
Thompsons Lane, Quayside,
Cambridge, Cambridgeshire,
England, CB5 8AG
+44 (0) 1223 361 008
www.greeneng.it

Hanovia
780 Buckingham Avenue, Slough,
Berkshire, England, SL1 4LA
+44 (0) 1753 515 300
www.hanovia.com

LH Stainless Ltd.
Towiemore, Drummuir, Keith,
Banffshire, Scotland, AB55 5JA
+44 (0) 1466 792 222
www.l-h-s.co.uk

Logistex
2700 Kettering Parkway,
Kettering, Northamptonshire,
England, NN15 6XR
+44 (0) 1536 480 600
www.logistex.com

Lorien Engineering Solutions Ltd
Millennium Court, First Avenue,
Centrum 100, Burton-on-Trent,
Staffordshire, England, DE14 2WH
+44 (0) 1283 485 100
www.lorienengineering.com

Niras
Sortemosevej 19, Allerod,
Denmark, 3450
+44 (0) 20 8569 7979
www.niras.com

Orapi Applied Ltd
15 Spring Road, Smethwick,
West Midlands, England, B66 1PT
+44 (0) 121 525 4000
www.orapiapplied.com

Pall Food and Beverage
5 Harbourgate Business Park,
Southampton Road, Portsmouth,
Hampshire, England, PO6 4BQ
+44 (0) 23 9233 8000
www.pall.com

Parker Hannifin Ltd
Tachbrook Park Drive, Warwick,
Warwickshire, England, CV34 6TU
+44 (0) 1926 317 878
www.parker.com

Scott Process Technology Ltd.
Ovenstone Works, Ovenstone,
Ansthruther, Fife, |
Scotland, KY10 2RR
+44 (0) 1333 311 394
www.scottprotec.com

Standfast Precision Engineering
Victoria Street, Craigellachie,
Banffshire, Scotland, AB38 9SR
+44 (0) 1340 881 371
www.standfast-engineering.com

Sterling Fluid Systems (UK) Ltd
QRC Europe House,
Second Avenue, Trafford Park,
Manchester, England, M17 1EE
+44 (0) 161 928 6371
www.sterlingfluid.com

Tomlinson Hall & Co Ltd.
Lagonda Road, Billingham,
North Yorkshire,
England, TS23 4JA
+44 (0) 1642 379 500
www.tomlinson-hall.co.uk

**Veolia Water Solutions
& Technologies**
Aqua House, Kings Court ,
Birmingham Business Park,
Birmingham, West Midlands,
England, B37 7YE
+44 (0) 203 567 7400
www.veoliawatertechnologies.co.uk

EQUIPMENT

Allen Associates (HPE) Ltd
Unit 7 Alpha Centre,
Stirling University innovation Park,
Stirling, Scotland, FK9 4NF
+44 (0) 1786 448777
www.allenhpe.co.uk

Axflow
Orion Park, Northfield Ave,
Ealing, London, Greater London,
England, W13 9SJ
+44 (0) 20 8579 2111
www.axflow.com/en-gb/gb

Buhler Ltd.
20 Atlantis Avenue,
London, Greater London,
England, E16 2BF
+44 (0) 2070 556 650
www.buhlergroup.com

BW Integrated Systems
1305 Lakeview Dr,
Romeoville, U.S.A., 60446 IL
+44 (0) 1302 711 056
www.bwintegratedsystems.com

Eastfield Process Equipment
Eastfield Farm, Tickhill,
Doncaster, South Yorkshire,
England, DN11 9JD
+44 (0) 1302 751 444
www.eastfieldprocessequipment.
co.uk

Hi-Line Services
56 Britannia Way, Lichfield,
Staffordshire, England, WS14 9UY
+44 (0) 1543 258 741
www.hilineservices.co.uk

Johnson Controls Inc.
5757N. Green Bay Ave., PO Box
591, Milwaukee, U.S.A., WI 53201
+1 414 524 1200
www.johnsoncontrols.co.uk

Seepex UK Ltd.
14 Memorial Rd, Yeovil, Somerset,
England, BA22 8RW
+44 (0) 1935 472 376
www.seepex.com

EQUIPMENT SUPPLIERS

Celloglas
Unit 12c Exeter Way,
Theale Commercial Estate,
Reading, Berkshire,
England, RG7 4AW
+44 (0) 1189 167 3003
www.celloglas.co.uk

Cockayne Ltd.
16 Flakefield, College Milton,
East Kilbride, Glasgow,
Scotland, G74 1PF
+44 (0) 1355 587 846
www.cockayne.co.uk

Ferrier Pumps
Unit 4 & 5, Barclayhill Place,
Protlethen, Aberdeen,
Aberdeenshire, Scotland, AB12 4PF
+44 (0) 1224 782 022
www.ferrierpumps.co.uk

Forsyths
Forsyths, Rothes, Moray,
Scotland, AB38 7AD
+44 (0) 1340 831 787
www.forsyths.com

**Fulton Boiler Works
(Great Britain) Ltd.**
5 Fernhurst Road, Fishponds,
Bristol, England, BS5 7FG
+44 (0) 117 972 3322
www.fulton.com

Klenzan Ltd
2 Cameron Court, Winwick Quay,
Warrington, Cheshire,
England, WA2 8RE
+44 (0) 1925 234 696
www.klenzan.co.uk

Label Apeel Ltd
Bo House, 17 Pinfold Road,
Thurmaston, Leicester,
Leicestershire, England, LE4 8AS
+44 (0) 116 231 4555
www.labelapeel.co.uk

Mettler-Toledo Ltd.
64 Boston Road, Beaumont Leys,
Leicester, Leicestershire,
England, LE4 1AW
+44 (0) 116 234 5222
www.mt.com

Northern Fabricators
1 Chanonry Industrial Estate,
Elgin, Moray, Scotland, IV30 6ND
+44 (0) 1343 546 139
www.norfabs.co.uk

SICK UK Ltd
Waldkirch House, 39 Hedley Road,
St Albans, Hertfordshire,
England, AL1 5BN
+44 (0) 1727 831 121
www.sick.co.uk

Stevenson Reeves Ltd
40 Oxgangs Bank, Edinburgh,
Midlothian, Scotland, EH13 9LH
+44 (0) 131 445 7151
www.stevenson-reeves.co.uk

GLASSWARE

Allied Glass Containers
69 South Accommodation Road,
Leeds, Leeds, England, LS10 1NQ
+44 (0) 1132 451 568
www.allied-glass.com

Burns Crystal Glass
11 Langlands Avenue,
Kelvin South Business Park,
East Kilbride, Glasgow, Ayrshire,
Scotland, G75 0YG
+44 (0) 1290 550 155
www.burnscrystal.co.uk

Dartington Crystal
Torrington, Devon,
England, EX38 7AN
+44 (0) 1805 626 262
www.dartington.co.uk

Enval Ltd
17-19 Taylor Street, Luton,
England, LU2 0EY
+44 (0) 845 299 7566
www.enval.com

Forever Crystal
12 Lancaster Rise, Belper,
Derbyshire, England, DE56 1HF
+44 (0) 1773 820 287
www.forevercrystal.co.uk

Glencairn Crystal
11 Langlands Avenue,
Kelvin South Business Park,
East Kilbride, South Lanarkshire,
Scotland, G75 0YG
+44 (0) 1355 279 717
www.glencairn.co.uk

Langham Glass
Greenway Lane, Fakenham,
Norfolk, England, NR21 8ET
+44 (0) 1328 863 500
www.langhamglass.co.uk

O-I Alloa
Glasshouse Loan,
Alloa, Clackmannshire,
Scotland, FK10 1PD
+44 (0) 1259 218 822
www.o-i.com

Owens-Illinois Inc
P.O. Box 6068, Edinburgh Way,
Harlow, Essex,
England, CM20 2 UG
+44 (0) 1279 422 222
www.o-i.com

Riedel Crystal
RSN UK Ltd, Lakeside House -
Trentham Office Village,
Trentham Lakes South,
Stoke-on-Trent,
Staffordshire, England, ST4 8GH
+44 (0) 1782 646 105
www.riedel.com

Saverglass
London, Greater London,
England, WF2 OYN
+44 (0) 113 322 1595
www.saverglass.com

Schott Glass
Drummond Road, Stafford,
Staffordshire, England, ST16 3EL
+44 (0) 1785 223 166
www.schott.com/uk

Urban Bar Ltd
The Glasshouse,
Highfields Business Park,
Kneesworth, Royston,
Hertfordshire,
England, SG8 5JT
+44 (0) 1763 500 131
www.urbanbar.com

William Croxson & Son Ltd
Alpha Place, Garth Road,
Morden, Surrey,
England, SM4 4LZ
+44 (0) 20 8337 2945
www.croxsons.com

Advanced Labelling Systems
Unit B Bandet Way, Thame,
Oxfordshire, England, OX9 3SJ
+44 (0) 1844 264 821
www.als.eu.com

AJS Labels
12 Arndale Rd.,
Lineside Ind.Estate,
Littlehampton, West Sussex,
England, BN17 7HD
+44 (0) 1903 731 212
www.ajslabels.com

Antalis
Baker & McKenzie LLP,
100 New Bridge Street, London,
England, EC4V 6JA
+44 (0) 3706 073 136
www.antalis.co.uk

CCL Decorative Sleeves
Rollesby Road, Hardwick
Industrial Estate, Kings Lynn,
Norfolk, England, PE30 4LS
+44 (0) 1553 769 319
www.ccllabel.com

Clarifoil
1, Holme Lane, Spondon, Derby,
Derbyshire, England, DE21 7BS
+44 (0) 1332 681 205
www.celanese.com/clarifoil

CS Labels
Unit D Bay 2, Willenhall Trading
Estate, Midacre Willenhall,
Willenhall, West Midlands,
England, WV13 2JW
+44 (0) 1902 365 840
www.cslabels.co.uk

Darley Ltd
Wellington Road, Burton-on-Trent,
Staffordshire, England, DE14 2AD
+44 (0) 1283 564 936
www.darleyLtd.co.uk

Denny Bros group
Kempson Way, Bury St Edmunds,
Suffolk, England, IP32 7AR
+44 (0) 1284 701 381
www.dennybros.com

G. & A. Kirsten Ltd.
Suite 8 Pelmark House,
11 Amwell End, Ware,
Hertfordshire, England, SG12 9HP
+44 (0) 1920 487 300
www.kirsten-group.com

Gavin Watson Printers
79-109 Glasgow Road, Glasgow,
Scotland, G72 0LY
+44 (0) 1698 826 000
www.gavinwatson.co.uk

Herma Labelling Systems
The Hollands Centre,
Hollands Road, Haverhill, Suffolk,
England, CB9 8PR
+44 (0) 1440 763 366
www.herma.co.uk

HSM UK Ltd
Burntwood Business Park,
Burntwood, Staffordshire,
England, WS7 9GJ
+44 (0) 1543 272 480
www.hsm.eu/uk

Labels Plus
Unit 22 Botany Business Park,
Macclesfield Road,
Whaley Bridge, Derbyshire,
England, SK23 7DQ
+44 (0) 1663 736 250
www.labelsplus.co.uk

Labelsco Ltd
Moat Way, Barwell, Leicestershire,
England, LE9 8EY
+44 (0) 1455 852 400
www.labelsco.co.uk

Logopak International Ltd
Enterprise House,
George Cayley Drive, Clifton
Moor Industrial Estate,
York, North Yorkshire,
England, YO30 4XE
+44 (0) 1904 692 333
www.logopak.com

Markem-Imaje Ltd
Brightgate House, Brightgate
Way, Trafford Park, Manchester,
England, M32 0TB
+44 (0) 1618 648 100
www.markem-imaje.co.uk

Mercian Labels
Unit 2 Plantslane business Park,
Burnswood, Staffordshire,
England, WS7 3GN
+44 (0) 1543 431 070
www.mercianlabels.com

Metsa Board
7 Frascati Way, Maidenhead,
Berkshire, England, ME4 4YG
+44 (0) 845 600 2293

Multi Labels Ltd
Sopwith Way,
Drayton Feild Industrial Estate,
Daventry, Northamptonshire,
England, NN11 8PB
+44 (0) 513 381 1480
www.multilabels.com

NSD International
Mayfield Industrial Estate,
Dalkeith, Midlothian,
Scotland, EH22 4AF
+44 (0) 131 654 4654
www.nsdinternational.com/en

Royston Labels
Unit 18, Orchard Road Industrial
Estate, Royston, Hertfordshire,
England, SG8 5HD
+44 (0) 1763 212 020
www.roystonlabels.co.uk

Smith & McLaurin Ltd
Cartside Mill, Kilbarchan,
Renfrewshire, Scotland, PA10 2AF
+44 (0) 1505 707 700
www.smcl.co.uk

Stribbons Ltd
The Linden Building, Regents
Park, Off Booth Drive,
Wallingborough,
Northamptonshire,
England, NN8 6GR
+44 (0) 1933 675 012
www.stribbons.com

The Label Makers
Labmak House, Prince Street,
Bradford, England, BD4 6HQ
+44 (0) 1274 681 151
www.labmak.co.uk

LABORATORY, ANALYSIS & TECHNICAL SUPPORT

Bellingham + Stanley Ltd.
Longfield Road,
North Farm Industrial Estate,
Tunbridge Wells, Kent,
England, TN2 3EY
+44 (0) 1892 500 400
www.bellinghamandstanley.com

Cara Technology
Randalls Road, Leatherhead,
Surrey, England, KT22 7RY
+44 (0) 1372 439 990
www.cara-online.com

Gas Measurement Instruments Ltd
Inchinnan Business Park, Renfrew,
Renfrewshire, Scotland, PA4 9RG
+44 (0) 141 812 3211
www.gmiuk.com

GSPK Design Ltd
Knaresborough Technology Park,
Manse Lane, Knaresborough,
North Yorkshire,
England, HG5 8LF
+44 (0) 1423 798 254
www.gspkdesign.ltd.uk

Integrated Scientific Ltd
Unit 3, Aspen Court,
Aspen Way, Centurion
Business Park, Templeborough,
Rotherham, South Yorkshire,
England, S60 1FB
+44 (0) 1709 830 493
www.integsci.com

Strathkelvin Instruments Ltd
Rowantree Avenue,
Motherwell, North Lanarkshire,
Scotland, ML1 5RX
+44 (0) 1698 730 400
www.strathkelvin.com

The Tintometer Ltd
Lovibond House, Sun Rise Way,
Amesbury, Wiltshire,
England, SP4 7GR
+44 (0) 1980 664 800
www.lovibondwater.com

LOGISTICS AND WAREHOUSING

Anchor Freight
109 Barrie Road,
Hillington, Glasgow, Lanarkshire,
Scotland, G52 4PX
+44 (0) 1418 922 080
www.anchor-freight.co.uk

Culina Ambient
Hellaby Lane, Rotherham,
England, S66 8HN
+44 (0) 1630 695407
www.culina.co.uk

Dachser
Northampton Logistics Centre,
Thomas Dachser Way, Brackmills,
Northamptonshire,
England, NN4 7HT
+44 (0) 1604 433 100
www.dachser.com

Hellmann Worldwide Logistics
Kuhlmann House, Lancaster Way,
Fradley Park, Lichfield,
England, WS13 8SX
+44 (0) 1543 443300
www.hellmann.net

JF Hillebrand UK
West Thurrock office, Dissegna
House, Weston Avenue, Grays,
Essex, England, RM20 3ZP
+44 (0) 1708 689 000
www.jfhillebrand.com

Macintyre Scott Xtra
Testwood House, Testwood Park,
Salisbury Road, Totton,
Hampshire, England, SO40 2RW
+44 (0) 2380 660 074
www.macintyrescott.com

Procurus Europa
9 Summit Business Park,
Langer Road, Felixstowe, Suffolk,
England, IP11 2JB
+44 (0) 1394 458 977
www.wsl-procurus.com/

RSM Solutions North East Ltd
11 Sowerby Way, Durham Lane
Industrial Park, Eaglescliffe,
Stockton-On-Tees,
England, TS16 0RB
+44 (0) 1642 791 315
www.rsm-solutions.co.uk

TDG McPherson
Fisherton Garage, Aberlour,
Banffshire, Scotland, AB38 9LB
+44 (0) 1340 871 401
www.mcpherson.ltd.uk

Wincanton
Methuen Park, Chippenham,
Wiltshire, England, SN14 0WT
+44 (0) 1249 710 000
www.wincanton.co.uk

MALTS, SUGARS & ADJUNCTS

Bairds Malt Ltd.
Station Maltings, Station Road,
Witham, Essex, England, CM8 2DU
+44 (0) 1376 513 566
www.bairds-malt.co.uk

Crisp Malting Group Ltd
Great Ryburgh, Fakenham,
Norfolk, England, NR21 7AS
+44 (0) 1328 829 391
www.crispmalt.com

DDW The Colour House
Trafford Park, Manchester,
Greater Manchester, England,
M17 1PA
+44 (0) 161 886 3345
www.ddwcolor.com

French & Jupp's
The Maltings, Stanstead Abbotts,
Ware, Hertfordshire,
England, SG12 8HG
+44 (0) 1920 870 015
www.frenchandjupps.com

Greencore Group
Midland Way,
Barlborough Links Business Park,
Barlborough, England, S43 4XA
+44 (0) 1909 545 900
www.greencore.com

Micronized Food Products
Standard Way, Northallerton,
North Yorkshire,
England, DL6 2XA
+44 (0) 1609 751 000
www.micronizedfoodproducts.
co.uk

Muntons plc
Cedars Maltings, Stowmarket,
Suffolk, England, IP14 2AG
+44 (0) 1449 618 300
www.muntons.com

Ragus Sugars (Manufacturing) Ltd.
830 Yeovil Road, Berkshire,
England, SL1 4JG
+44 (0) 1753 575 353
www.ragus.co.uk

Simpsons Malt Ltd
Tweed Valley Maltings, Berwick-
upon-Tweed, Northumberland,
England, TD15 2UZ
+44 (0) 1289 330 033
www.simpsonsmalt.co.uk

Thomas Fawcett & Sons Ltd.
EastField Lane, Castleford,
West Yorkshire, England, WF10 4LE
+44 (0) 1977 552 460
www.fawcett-maltsters.co.uk

Tuckers Maltings
Teign Road, Newton Abbot,
Devon, England, TQ12 4AA
+44 (0) 1626 334 002
edwintucker.co.uk

Warminster Maltings Ltd
39 Pound Street, Warminster,
Wiltshire, England, BA12 8NN
+44 (0) 1985 212 014
www.warminster-malt.co.uk

PACKAGING SUPPLIERS

A & S Packing
Block 15, Vale of Leven Industrial
Estate, Dumbarton, Glasgow,
Scotland, G82 3PD
+44 (0) 1389 768 660
www.aspacking.co.uk

AEC Packaging
L-1-10, Kuchai Business Park,
No.2, Jalan 1/127, Off Jalan
Kuchai Lama, Kuala Lumpur,
Malaysia, 58200
+603 7494 1268
www.aecworldwide.com

Aegg Creative Packaging
Fellows House, Royce Close,
West Portway Industrial Estate,
Andover, Hampshire,
England, SP10 3TS
+44 (0) 1722 416 401
www.aegg.co.uk

Allpack Packaging
Midddlemore Lane West,
Walsall, West Midlands,
England, WS9 8BH
+44 (0) 1922 472 400
www.allpackpackaging.co.uk

Antalis Packaging
41 Road One Winsford Industrial
Estate, Winsford, Cheshire,
England, CW7 3QB
+44 (0) 8702 411 466
www.antalispackaging.co.uk

APi Laminates Ltd
Second Avenue,
Poynton Industrial Estate,
Stockport, Cheshire,
England, SK12 1ND
+44 (0) 1625 650 500
www.apigroup.com

Avina International
First Floor, Woburn Court,
2 Railton Road, Woburn Road
Industrial Estate, Bedford,
England, MK42 7PN
+44 (0) 7801 057 666
www.avinainternational.co.uk

Ball
Tongwell, Delaware Drive,
Milton Keynes, Greater London,
England, MK15 8HG
+44 (0) 1908 517 600
www.ball.com

Beatson Clark
The Glass Works,
Greasbrough Road, Rotherham,
South Yorkshire, England, S60 1TZ
+44 (0) 1709 828 141
www.beatsonclark.co.uk

Bell Packaging
Barratt Industrial Park,
Airport Way, Luton, Bedfordshire,
England, LU2 9NH
+44 (0) 1582 459 292
www.bellpackaging.com

Billerudkorsnas UK Ltd
11 The Triangle, Enterprise Way,
Nottingham, Nottinghamshire,
England, NG2 1AE
+44 (0) 1158 229 950
www.b.comillerudkorsnas

Burgopak
Units A&D, Flat Iron Yard,
14 Ayres Street, London,
Greater London,
England, SE1 1ES
+44 (0) 20 7089 1950
www.burgopak.com

Cartotecnica Ltd
2 Debdale Road,
Wellingborough,
Nottinghamshire,
England, NN8 5AA
www.cartotecnicarossi.it/eng

Castle Colour Group
3 Morgan Way, Norwich,
Norfolk, England, NR5 9JJ
+44 (0) 1603 741 278
www.castlecolour.co.uk

CBT Packaging Ltd
Unit D2 Zenith, Paycocke Road,
Basildon, Essex,
England, SS14 3DW
+44 (0) 1268 247 380
www.cbtpackaging.co.uk

Ceva Logistics
Excelsior Road,
Ashby-de-la-Zouch,
England, LE65 1NU
+44 (0) 3305 877 000
www.cevalogistics.com

Charapak Ltd
Salcombe Road,
Meadow Lane Industrial Estate,
Alfreton, Derbyshire,
England, DE55 7RG
+44 (0) 1773 835 735
www.charapak.co.uk

Charpak Ltd
30 St Peters Road,
Huntingdon, Cambridgeshire,
England, PE29 7DG
+44 (0) 1480 434 434
www.charpak.uk

Clarke Rubicon
Telford Way, Stephenson
Industrial Estate, Coalville,
Leicestershire, England, LE67 3HE
+44 (0) 1530 513 700
www.clarke-rubicon.co.uk

Complete Co-Packing Services
Unit 6, Ynysboeth Estate,
Mountain Ash, Abercynon,
Rhondda, Wales, CF45 4SF
+44 (0) 1443 740 786
www.complete-copacking.co.uk

Coveris
Pinchbeck, England,
+44 (0) 1775 717 300
www.coveris.co.uk

Cullen Packaging
Dawsholm Industrial Estate,
10 Dawsholm Ave, Glasgow,
Lanarkshire, Scotland, G20 0TS
+44 (0) 1419 452 222
www.cullen.co.uk

Domino Printing Sciences Plc
Trafalgar Way, Bar Hill,
Cambridge, England, CB23 8TU
+44 (0) 1954 782 551
www.domino-printing.com

DS Smith Packaging
Units 6&7, Newbridge Trading
Estate, Newbridge Close, Bristol,
England, BS4 4AX
+44 (0) 845 260 70 80
www.dssmith.com

Duncan Print
Broadwater House, Mundells,
Welwyn Garden City,
Hertfordshire, England, AL7 1EU
+44 (0) 1707 336 271
www.duncanprint.co.uk

Elanders
Unit B, Merlin Way,
Newcastle Upon Tyne, Tyne &
Wear, England, NE27 0QG
+44 (0) 1912 800 400
www.elanders.com

Eska Graphic Board Uk Ltd
PO Box 90, Sappemeer,
Netherlands, 9610
+31 598 318 911
www.eska.com

Esko UK (Solihull)
The Rhodium, Blythe Valley Park,
Solihull, West Midlands,
England, B90 8AS
+44 (0) 121 667 4200
www.esko.com

Essentra
Giltway, Giltbrook, Nottingham,
Nottinghamshire, England, NG16 2GT
+44 (0) 115 975 9000
www.essentra.com

Falconer Print & Packaging
Unit G5 Lowfields Business Park,
Elland, West Yorkshire,
England, HX5 9HB
+44 (0) 1422 373 377
www.falconerprint.co.uk

FMP
Unit 8 Hightown,
Whitecross Industrial Estate,
Lancaster, Lancashire,
England, LA1 4XS
+44 (0) 152 468 737
flexible-medical.co.uk

Foilco
Enterprise Way, Lowton St Mary's,
Cheshire, England, WA3 2BP
+44 (0) 1942 262 622
www.foilco.co.uk

G F Smith
Lockwood Street, Hull,
East Riding of Yorkshire,
England, HU2 0HL
+44 (0) 1482 323 503
www.gfsmith.com

Gaasch Pack Ltd
Flat G/2, Imperial Tower, 1
Meadowside Quay Square,
Glasgow, Glasgow, Scotland, G11 6BS
+44 (0) 1413 393 344
www.gaaschpack.eu

Garthwest Ltd.
13 Rotterdam Road,
Sutton Fields, Kingston Upon Hull,
East Riding of Yorkshire,
England, HU7 0XA
+44 (0) 1482 825 121
www.garthwest.com

Gilmour & Dean / Eurostampa
24 Clydehom Road, Clydeside
Industrial Estate, Glasgow,
Scotland, G14 0QQ
+44 (0) 141 272 8500
www.eurostampa.com/en

Glossop-Cartons
Raymond Joseph Works, Unit 5,
Haigh Ave, Whitehill Industrial
Estate, Reddish, Stockport,
England, SK4 1NU
+44 (0) 1614 803 568

Granby Marketing Services
Stanley Street, Blackburn,
England, BB1 3BW
+44 (0) 1254 682 702
www.granbymarketing.com

Graphic Packaging
Interlink Park, Bardon,
Leicestershire, England, LE67 1PE
+44 (0) 1530 518 200
ww.graphicpkgeurope.com

Herbert Walkers Ltd
113 Dockfield Road, Shipley, West
Yorkshire, England, BD17 7AS
+44 (0) 1274 531 828
www.herbertwalkers.co.uk

Hewlett-Packard
Amen Corner, Cain Road,
Bracknell, Berkshire,
England, RG12 1HN
+44 (0) 3452 704 567
www.hp.com

HH Deluxe Packaging
49 Leigh Road, Eastleigh,
Hampshire, England, SO50 9DF
+44 (0) 2380 625 864
www.hhdeluxepackaging.com

Hunter Sourcing
Harpenden Hall, Southdown
Road, Harpenden, Hertfordshire,
England, AL5 1TE
+44 (0) 1582 711 877
www.huntersourcing.net

Ibis Packaging Solutions
Unit 10 Colthrop Business Park,
Clothrop Lane, Thatcham,
Buckinghamshire,
England, RG14 9NB
+44 (0) 1639 890 609
www.ibispackaging.co.uk

iDi Pac Ltd
5 Ridgeway Office Park,
Bedford Road, Petersfield,
England, GU32 3QF
+44 (0) 1420 538 055
www.idipac.com

IDP Direct Great Britain
Norfolk House, 4 Station Road,
St. Ives, England, PE27 5AF
+44 (0) 1487 802 082
the-idp-group.com

Iggesund Paperboard
Workington Mill, Workington,
Cumbria, England, CA14 1JX
+44 (0) 1900 601000
www.iggesund.com/en

Interlok Packaging Ltd
Gareloch Industrial Estate,
Port Glasgow, Renfrewshire,
Scotland, PA14 5UG
+44 (0) 1475 707 669
www.interlokpackaging.co.uk

Interscope Productions Ltd
47 St Saviours Road, Croydon,
Surrey, England, CR0 2XE
+44 (0) 2032 876 996
www.interscopeproductions.com

INWK
600 West Chicago Avenue,
Chicago , U.S.A., IL 60654
+1 866 766 5176
www.inwk.com

Jacob White Packaging Ltd
Riverside Industrial Estate,
Unit F, Riverside Way, Dartford,
Kent, England, DA1 5BY
+44 (0) 1322 272 531
www.jacobwhite.com

**James Cropper Speciality
Papers Ltd**
Burneside Mills, Kendal,
Cumbria, England, LA9 6PZ
+44 (0) 1539 722 002
www.jamescropper.com

Jenton Intl
9/10 Ardglen Industrial Estate,
Ardglen Road, Whitchurch,
Bedfordshire, England, RG28 7BB
+44 (0) 1256 892 194
www.jenton.co.uk

Keenpac
Keenpac, Centurion Way,
Meridian Business Park, Leicester,
Leicestershire, England, LE19 1WH
+44 (0) 1162 890 900
www,keenpac.com

Kingsmoor Packaging
Cary Court, Bancombe Road
Industrial Estate, Somerton,
Somerset, England, TA11 6SB
+44 (0) 1458 273 001
www.kingsmoorpackaging.co.uk

KTEC Group
93B Heming Road, Washford
Industrial Estate, Redditch,
Worcestershire, England, B98 0EA
+44 (0) 1527 529 713
www.ktecgroup.co.uk

Law Print Pack
4 Rhino Court, Station View,
Hazel Grove, Stockport, Cheshire,
England, SK7 5ER
+44 (0) 1614 407 302
lawprintpack.co.uk

Lemonpath
Unit 1B, Wanlip Road Industrial
Estate, Wanlip Road, Syston,
Leicestershire, England, LE12 9TQ
+44 (0) 1162 645 000
www.lemonpath.co.uk

Leo Luxe
16 Wang Hoi Road, Level 9, Telford
House, Hong Kong, 120608
+852 251 306 98
www.webpackaging.com

Linx Printing Technologies
Linx House, 8 Stocks Bridge Way,
Compass Point Business Park, St
Ives, Cambridgeshire, England,
PE27 3IA
+44 (0) 1480 302 100
www..linxglobal.com

Macfarlane Packaging
Siskin Parway East,
Middlemarch Business Park,
Coventry, West Midlands,
England, CV3 4PE
+44 (0) 8002 888 822
shop.macfarlanepackaging.com

Mailway Packaging Solutions
12-16 Pitcliffe Way,
Upper Castle Street, West
Bowling, Bradford,
England, BD5 7SG
+44 (0) 1274 720 019
www.mailway.co.uk

Martek Industries
12B Ridings Industrial Estate,
Eastern Ways, Cannock,
Staffordshire, England, WS11 7SF
+44 (0) 1543 502 202
www.martekindustries.co.uk

McLaren Packaging
Gareloch Road Industrial Estate,
Port Glasgow, Glasgow,
Scotland, PA14 5XH
+44 (0) 1475 745 246
www.mclarenpackaging.com

MDA Ltd
Client Support Centre,
Walker Park, Blackamoor Road,
Blackburn, England, BB1 2LG
+44 (0) 1254 278 279
www.mdaLtd.co.uk

Menshen Packaging
Unit 92, Portmanmoor Industrial
Estate, Cardiff, Glamorgan,
Wales, CF24 9HB
+44 (0) 2920 473 147
www.menshen.co.uk

Message on a Bottle
West Wemyss, Kirkcaldy, Fife,
Scotland, KY1 4SN
+44 (0) 1592 655 629
www.messageonabottle.biz

MSO Cleland Packaging
399 Castlereagh Road, Belfast,
Northern Ireland, BT5 6QP
+44 (0) 28 9040 0200
www.mso.co.uk

161

Multi Packaging Solutions
885 Third Avenue, 28th Floor,
New York, NY, U.S.A., 10022
+1 646 885 0150
www.multipkg.com

Multi Packaging Solutions
14 Colthrop Business Park,
Colthrop Way, Thatcham,
England, RG19 4LW
+44 (0) 1635 290500
www.multipkg.com

NMC
Tafarnaubach Industrial Estate,
Tredegard, Wales, NP22 3AA
+44 (0) 1495 713 266
www.nmc-uk.com

OKI Systems (UK) Ltd
Blays House, Wick Road, Egham,
Surrey, England, TW20 0HJ
+44 (0) 1784 274 300
www.oki.co.uk

Packology Ltd
27 Fitzroy Drive, Cherque Farm,
Lee-On-The-Solent, Hampshire,
England, PO13 8LY
+44 (0) 7971 508 421
www.packology.com

Pallite
60 Sinclair Drive, Park Farm North
industrial Estate, Wellingborough,
Northamptonshire,
England, NN8 6UY
+44 (0) 1933 283 920
www.paperpallet.co.uk

Penn Packaging
Harkstead Hall Barn, Harkstead,
Ipswich, Suffolk, England, IP9 1DB
+44 (0) 1473 893 990
www.penn-packaging.co.uk

Pollard Boxes
Feldspar Close, Enderby,
Leicestershire, England, LE19 4SD
+44 (0) 116 275 2666
www.pollardboxes.co.uk

Polmac (UK)
3 The Briars, Warrenwood, High
Wycombe, Buckinghamshire,
England, HP11 1ED
+44 (0) 1494 533 857
www.polmacuk.com

Polypackaging
2/4 Whitfield Drive,
The Heathfield Industrial Estate,
Ayr, Ayrshire, Scotland, KA8 FRX
+44 (0) 1292 262 473
polypackaging.co.uk

Pont Packaging
Unit 2, Newtons Court, Crossways
Business Park, Dartford, Kent,
England, DA2 6QL
+44 (0) 1322 291 111
www.pontuk.com

Progress Packaging
The Mill, 150 Penistone Road,
Huddersfield, England, HD8 8JQ
+44 (0) 1484.608.600
www.progresspackaging.co.uk

RPC Group
Sapphire House, Crown Way,
Rushden, England, NN10 6FB
+44 (0) 1933 416 528
www.rpc-bpi.com

RPC Group
Sapphire House, Crown Way, Rushden,
Northamptonshire, NN10 6FB
+44 (0) 1933 416 528
www.rpc-group.com

Sangobeg Ltd (Broxburn)
56 Torridon Road, Broughtyferry,
Dundee, Scotland, DD5 3JH
+44 (0) 1382 770 030

SCA Packaging
Skepparplasten 1, Sundsvall,
Sweden, SE-851 88
www.sca.com/en

Signet Branding
Innovation House, Bakewell Road,
Orton Southgate, Peterborough,
Cambridgeshire, England, PE2 6XU
+44 (0) 1733 396080
www.signetbranding.com

Simply Cartons
Perry Road, Nottingham,
Nottinghamshire,
England, NG5 1GQ
+44 (0) 1159 422 112
www.simplycartons.co.uk

Smithers Pira
Cleeve Road, Leatherhead,
Surrey, England, KT22 7RU
+44 (0) 1372 802 000
www.smitherspira.com

Sonoco Trident (Image Linx UK Ltd)
Julius Way, Station Park,
Lowmore Road, Kirkby,
Nottinghamshire,
England, NG17 7RB
+44 (0) 1623 689 500
www.imagelinx.co.uk

Staeger Clear Packaging Ltd
Unit 1, Swallowgate Business
Park, Coventry, Warwickshire,
England, CV6 4BL
+44 (0) 2476 581 197
www.staegerclear.co.uk

Strand Paper & Board
100 Main Street, Bingley,
West Yorkshire,
England, BD16 2JH
+44 (0) 1274 566 748
www.strand-paper.co.uk

Tetra Pak Ltd
The Foundation Herons Way,
Chester Business Park, Chester,
England, CH4 9QS
+44 (0) 1978 834 000
www.tetrapak.com

The Box UK
Central Boulevard,
Blyrth Valley Business Park,
Solihull, West Midlands, B90 8AG
+44 (0) 1676 492 902
www.theboxuk.co.uk

The OPM Group
The Colour Box, Gelderd Road,
Leeds, England, LS12 6TG
+44 (0) 113 231 1000
opmgroup.co.uk

The Wilkins Group
Private Road Number 1,
Colwick Industrial Estate,
Nottingham, Nottinghamshire,
England, NG3 2JQ
+44 (0) 1159 896 000
www.wilkins.co.uk

Tinpac
21A Newton Road, Swansea,
Gwynedd, Wales, SA3 4AS
+44 (0) 1792 369 855
www.tinpac.com

Tinware Direct
Crowhill Farm, Ravensden Rd,
Wilden, Bedford, Bedfordshire,
England, MK44 2QS
+44 (0) 1234 772 001
tinwaredirect.com

TRM Packaging
Red Cat Lane, Burscough,
Lancashire, England, L40 0SY
+44 (0) 1704 892 811
www.trmpack.co.uk

Tullis Russell
Church Street, Bollington,
Macclesfield, Cheshire,
England, SK10 5QF
+44 (0) 1625 578 295
www.tullisrussell.com

Tungate Group
Boorkhouse Way, Cheadle,
Staffordshire, England, ST10 1SR
+44 (0) 1538 755 755
www.tungate.co.uk

Vassi Group
20 Woodside Place, Glasgow,
Lanarkshire, Scotland, G3 7QF
+44 (0) 7557 503850
www.vassigroup.com

Vetroplas Packaging
Chalk Hill Cottage, 19 Rosary
Road, Norwich, Norfolk,
England, NR1 1SZ
+44 (0) 1603 305 953
www.vetroplas.com

Visican Ltd
115 Phillips Street, Aston,
West Midlands, England, B6 4PT
+44 (0) 1213 598 800

Windmill Print
Denmore Place, Bridge of Don,
Aberdeen, Aberdeenshire,
Scotland, AB23 8JS
+44 (0) 1224 828 000
www.windmilprint.com

Wine Emotion UK
The Lynchets, Bagnor, Newbury,
Berkshire, England, RG20 8AQ
+44 (0) 1635 282 230
www.wineemotionuk.com

Winter & Company UK Ltd
Stonehill, Stukeley Mead
Industrial Estate,
Huntingdon , Cambridgeshire,
England, PE29 6ED
+44 (0) 1480 377 177
www.winter-company.com

Woodway UK
Mallard Close, Earls Barton,
Northamptonshire, England, NN6 0JF
+44 (0) 1604 812 678
www.woodwayuk.com

Yorkshire Packaging Systems
Woodkirk Freight Terminal,
Quarry Lane, Woodkirk, West
Yorkshire, England, WF12 7JJ
+44 (0) 1924 441 355
www.yps.co.uk

Zenith Print & Packaging Ltd
Gellihirion Industrial Estate,
Treforest, Pontypridd, Cardiff,
Wales, CF37 5SX
+44 (0) 1443 841 166
www.zenithprinting.com

PROCESS AIDS

Murphy & Son Ltd
Alpine Street, Old Basford,
Nottingham, Nottinghamshire,
England, NG6 0HQ
+44 (0) 1159 785 494
www.murphyandson.co.uk

PQ Corporation
Valleybrooke Corporate Center,
300 Lindenwood Drive, Malvern,
Pennsylvania, USA, 19355-1740
+1 6106 514 200
www.pqcorp.com

RAW MATERIALS

Joseph Flach & Sons Ltd
22 Maxwell Road, Peterborough,
Cambridgeshire,
England, PE2 7JD
+44 (0) 1733 371 221
www.josephflach.co.uk

Lupofresh Ltd.
Stocks Farm, Suckley,
Worcestershire,
England, WR6 5EH
+44 (0) 1886 884 202
www.britishhops.org.uk

YEAST SUPPLIERS

AB Mauri
Stockholm Road, Sutton Fields
Industrial Estate, Hull, East
Yorkshire,
England, HU7 OXW
+44 (0) 1482 833 133
www.abmauriukandireland.com

Index